THE ART OF HEALTHY EATING AND LIVING WITH CHIVA-SOM

THE ART OF HEALTHY EATING AND LIVING WITH

CHIVA-SOM

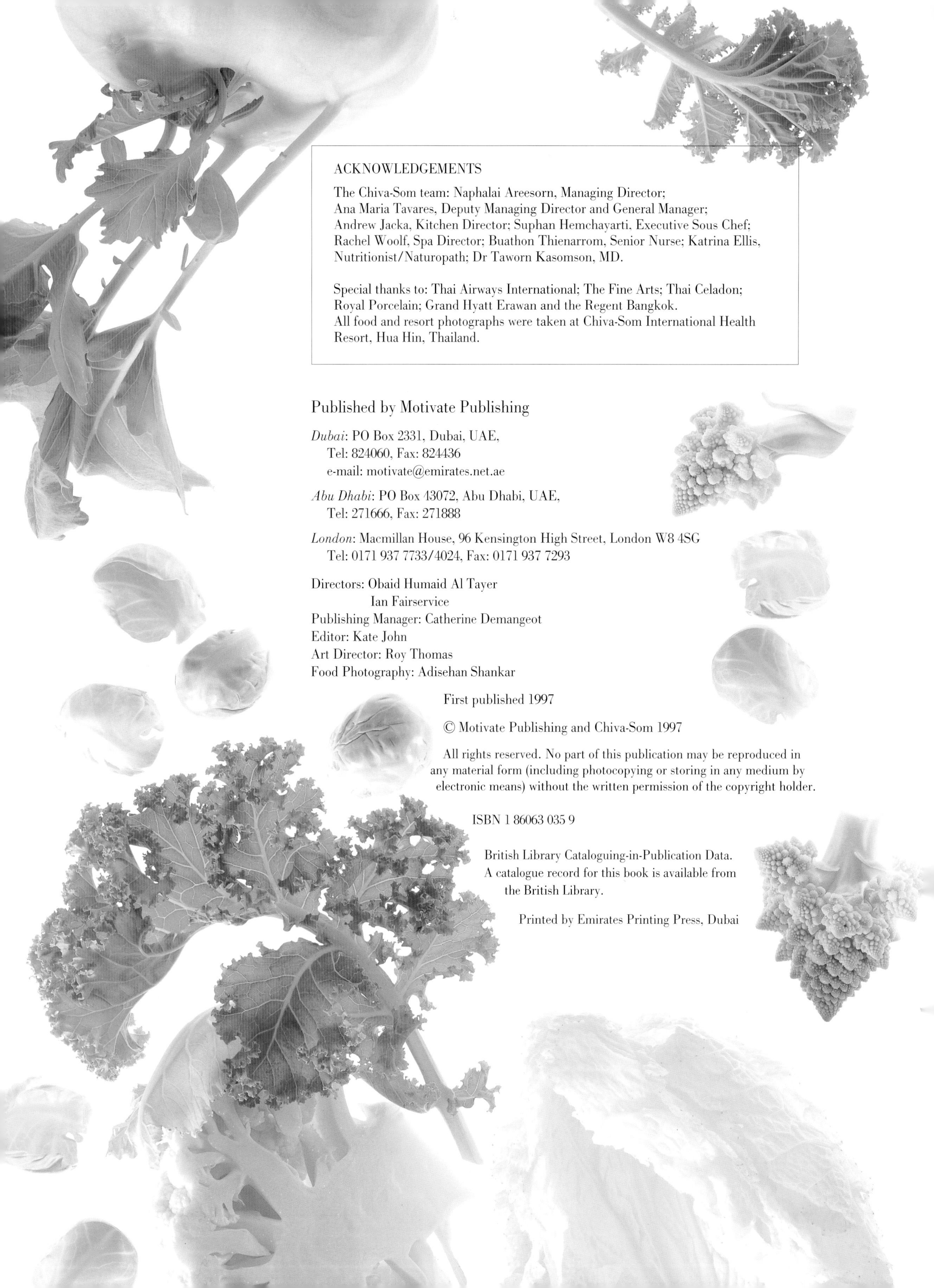

ACKNOWLEDGEMENTS

The Chiva-Som team: Naphalai Areesorn, Managing Director; Ana Maria Tavares, Deputy Managing Director and General Manager; Andrew Jacka, Kitchen Director; Suphan Hemchayarti, Executive Sous Chef; Rachel Woolf, Spa Director; Buathon Thienarrom, Senior Nurse; Katrina Ellis, Nutritionist/Naturopath; Dr Taworn Kasomson, MD.

Special thanks to: Thai Airways International; The Fine Arts; Thai Celadon; Royal Porcelain; Grand Hyatt Erawan and the Regent Bangkok.
All food and resort photographs were taken at Chiva-Som International Health Resort, Hua Hin, Thailand.

Published by Motivate Publishing

Dubai: PO Box 2331, Dubai, UAE,
Tel: 824060, Fax: 824436
e-mail: motivate@emirates.net.ae

Abu Dhabi: PO Box 43072, Abu Dhabi, UAE,
Tel: 271666, Fax: 271888

London: Macmillan House, 96 Kensington High Street, London W8 4SG
Tel: 0171 937 7733/4024, Fax: 0171 937 7293

Directors: Obaid Humaid Al Tayer
Ian Fairservice
Publishing Manager: Catherine Demangeot
Editor: Kate John
Art Director: Roy Thomas
Food Photography: Adisehan Shankar

First published 1997

ISBN 1 86063 035 9

British Library Cataloguing-in-Publication Data.
A catalogue record for this book is available from the British Library.

Printed by Emirates Printing Press, Dubai

CONTENTS

Healthy Living

A Holistic Way to Look at Life

Water is one of the most nurturing elements of a holistic lifestyle – the mind, body and spirit benefit in different ways from its life-giving properties and intrinsic beauty.

Yoga (far right) helps to balance the whole well-being of a person, by enhancing the body's natural energy flow, the mind's spatial consciousness, and the spirit's desire to focus positively.

Many of us view ourselves almost like machines and put the various aspects of our lives into separate compartments. Provided our bodies give us no trouble we pay them little attention. However if one of the parts goes wrong we get it fixed in much the same way as we service our cars. Our minds, our spirits, our lifestyle and the ways in which we relate to other people and the rest of the world do not feature much, if at all, in this mechanistic scheme of things.

But there is another way of looking at ourselves and our lives. According to this approach our bodies, minds, spirits, the way we live and the world around us, are seen as an integrated whole. Throughout the ages and in every culture wise men and women have concluded that the secret of a long, healthy and happy existence lies in looking at life in this way. Many people today are rediscovering the basic principles of living that lie behind this holistic approach, and in the process, are leading healthier, more fulfilling lives.

The Holistic Approach in Practice

The holistic approach to life is quite simple. It involves caring for the basic needs of your body, mind and spirit and seeking an equilibrium between them. On a purely physical level the holistic approach means making sure that you provide your body with the right amount of fresh, nutritious, health-giving food and ensure that it gets the correct balance of activity, rest and relaxation.

On a mental level it means paying attention to the way you think and making sure that your mind too is balanced between work, rest and play. For, according to the holistic approach, the mind affects the body, and the way you feel and think is reflected in how you look.

WHO ARE YOU?

As part of an overall holistic approach to life, Chiva-Som embraces three basic principles:

- **You are what you are by what you experience in life.**
- **You are what you are by what you eat.**
- **You are what you are by what you inherit from your ancestors.**

The last part of the holistic philosophy is about becoming aware of another, more spiritual dimension. It is about perceiving the unity between yourself and other humans and the world around you.

There is no single way to reach this level of awareness, nor is it something you consciously have to try to make happen. Many people do it themselves by practising meditation, by contemplating beautiful surroundings or by listening to music. Others are helped along the path by therapies that work on the mind and the body such as hydrotherapy, reflexology, massage or aromatherapy. However you get there, what you will attain is a feeling of being completely at peace.

KEEPING A BALANCE DULAYAPHAP BUMBUD (EQUILIBROPATHY)

Keeping a balance between body, mind and spirit is central to the Chiva-Som philosophy. In Eastern medicine the smooth flow of Chi, the body's life force energy, is

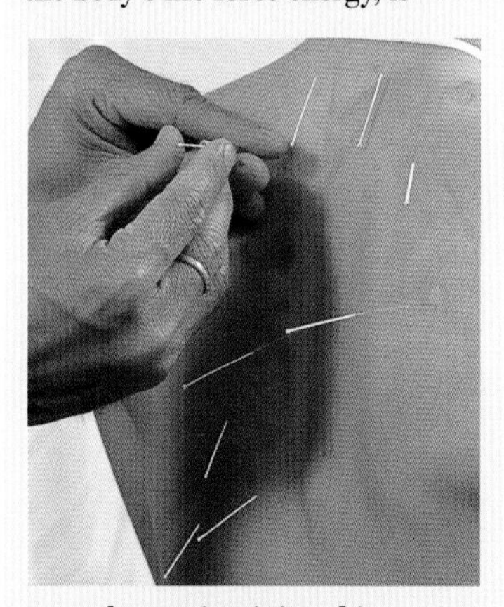

central to maintaining this balance. Posture is central to well-being. Equilibropathy is a system of therapy that uses acupuncture techniques, special exercises and manipulation of the spine to help maintain the flow of Chi and keep the body in healthy balance. The therapy can be used to help you stay healthy and therapeutically to treat asthma, migraine, sore muscles, sinus congestion, vertigo, stiff joints and any condition in which there is lowered immunity.

Looking at the Basics The Breath of Life

Breathing is literally the most vital act we perform, yet it is something to which most of us pay little attention. When we breathe we draw life-giving oxygen from the air around us and expel carbon dioxide and other wastes from our bodies. Oxygen is the source of life. All organisms need this vital element and human beings are no exception. One reason why aerobic exercise is so important is that it forces us to breathe more deeply and improves the body's use of oxygen.

Learning how to breathe fully and consciously – and not quickly and shallowly from your chest as many people do – is one of the most important steps you can take to improve your sense of well-being and zest. Proper breathing from the diaphragm, the domed sheet of muscle that separates the chest from the abdomen, also helps to develop awareness of the unity of mind, body and spirit.

The Power of Breathing

Breathing properly helps energise all your tissues, calms your heart rate, lowers blood pressure, boosts resistance to disease, lifts mood and improves sleep. Practise this method of breathing for ten minutes, a couple of times a day, and it will become automatic. Here's how to start:

1. Lie comfortably on a bed or the floor, supporting the small of your back and your neck with cushions if need be. Focus your attention on your breathing and become aware of how you breathe for a few minutes.

2 Place one hand on your upper chest and one on your abdomen and breathe out slowly and fully. Feel your abdomen flatten as you do so. If you are doing it properly there should be very little movement in your upper chest. Now pause for a couple of seconds and become aware of the empty still space inside before you take an inward breath.

3 Inhale slowly through your nose, feeling the breath stream into your lungs and expanding your abdomen. Pause again for a second or two before you exhale.

Some people find it helps to imagine their breath completing a circle as they breathe slowly in – and then out. Others imagine their breath as a stream of light or colour infusing their body.

Once you get into the habit of breathing in this way you can use it whenever you feel stressed, for example, if you are stuck in a traffic jam or waiting in a queue.

OXYGEN – THE SOURCE OF LIFE

- **We can go without food for up to half a year, without fluid for 5 to 7 days but without oxygen we can only exist for a matter of a few minutes.**
- **Oxygen makes up 21 per cent of the air we breathe.**
- **Without oxygen to convert the energy stored in food, the most delicious and carefully-balanced meals are of absolutely no use.**
- **Oxygen is vital for cell metabolism – all the complex biochemical processes that are going on in our cells every second, day and night to enable us to live.**
- **Oxygen is needed to cleanse our bodies and clear out harmful toxins.**

Health – The Inside Story

True health begins within the body's own powerhouses – the trillions of cells from which we are each made. Each cell is like a mini-furnace fuelled by oxygen. Cells stoked with oxygen function smoothly and efficiently, enabling us to feel bright and lively, both mentally and physically; cells starved of oxygen falter, making us tired and sluggish.

When you are unfit and sedentary, cells produce energy without using oxygen by means of a mechanism known as anaerobic metabolism. Glucose, drawn from stores in the muscles is gobbled up and used for kindling. Because the cells are deprived of oxygen they tire quickly and produce waste products that inhibit their smooth working. And because this way of making energy does not involve using fat as fuel, it is harder to lose weight.

Breathing properly and regular exercise – the sort that pushes up your heart rate and makes you sweat and pant slightly – increases the cells' capacity to take in and use oxygen, by means of a mechanism known as aerobic metabolism. Instead of drawing glucose from the muscles the cells use stored fat as kindling. This improves delivery of oxygen to the cells, burns up fat, helps you stay slim and helps you stay young longer.

Because this process is so efficient the cells produce less waste, allowing our muscles to power us through each day and providing a super-abundance of energy and vitality.

By concentrating on a regular work-out that suits your own body's needs, you will soon gain greater control of your aerobic metabolism. Swimming will naturally boost your rate of breathing while toning the whole body.

PERFECT POSTURE

A balanced posture is vital to good health and to maintain the flow of Chi, the body's life force energy.

- **Keep your abdomen pulled in to straighten your back whenever you sit, stand, walk, run or work.**
- **Pull your shoulders back as though you were trying to get the shoulder blades to meet.**
- **Draw your chin backwards to straighten your neck.**

THE MAGIC OF MOVEMENT
EXERCISE – THE KEY TO ENERGY AND ZEST

With the action-packed, high-energy lives we all lead today, exercise is vital. Sitting around all day and taking the car instead of walking compresses the spine, leading to poor posture. This in turn causes muscular aches and pains, and cramps the internal organs so they cannot function properly. Without exercise our skin looks pale and unhealthy, fat accumulates in and around muscles, and fatty deposits under the skin cause stretchmarks and dimpling. Meanwhile, muscles that are not used shrink and waste, giving you a lumpy outline. Your body is more prone to injury and wears out faster.

When you are young your body may just about tolerate an inactive way of life. However, as you get older, your unhealthy lifestyle may start to manifest itself in a whole range of health problems from digestive disorders, to aching joints, high blood pressure and poor circulation. Eventually heart attacks, strokes and other serious diseases such as rheumatoid arthritis, diabetes and cancer may develop.

The way to combat these negative effects is quite simple: more activity. Exercise improves circulation giving your skin a healthy glow and brightening your eyes; it also tones and firms the muscles resulting in a slimmer, younger-looking you.

Exercise helps disperse stress chemicals such as adrenalin, which otherwise accumulate in tissues and can cause spasms and furring of the arteries which slow circulation to the body and the brain, and can ultimately affect the heart. At the same time, chemicals released when you exercise keep your mind alert and sharp and give you a more positive outlook.

GETTING STARTED

Getting fit does not involve making vast, unsustainable changes to your lifestyle. There is no need to rush out and buy leotards or fancy footwear – unless you want to, of course. All you need to do is decide that you want to become fit and make a simple plan that fits into your daily routine. Ideally,

Cycling to and from work, or exploring off-road routes with friends is the ideal form of exercise for all ages and fitness abilities. Without having to be competitive, it is nonetheless stimulating both physically and mentally, wherever you pedal to.

you should exercise three times a week for at least 20 minutes at a time.

The key to sticking to your exercise plan is to ease yourself into it gently. Hurling yourself into a frantic programme of activity, when all you usually do is sit in a chair or drive, is counterproductive. You risk sore, injured muscles and are likely to become frustrated and disillusioned.

You are more likely to stick to a fitness routine if you choose an activity you really enjoy such as dancing, swimming, walking, cycling, playing tennis. Exercising with a friend or partner makes it more fun and helps keep up flagging motivation.

If you are unused to exercise you can expect to huff and puff a bit when you first start being more active. This is not because there is anything wrong with your heart or lungs; it is a sign that your muscles are not using oxygen efficiently. As you get fitter and your muscles become more efficient, you will find this less of a problem.

Pacing Yourself

You know that your cells are using oxygen when you begin to breathe harder, feel your heart beating faster and begin to work up a sweat. It is important to keep an eye on how hard you are exercising to make sure you are working at the right pace for you and not overdoing it.

The Talk Test

The simplest method of measuring exercise intensity is the 'talk test'. If you can talk while you are exercising without gasping for breath then the level you are working at is about right for you. If you cannot talk because you are breathing too heavily, you should reduce your effort until you can talk.

A calm environment in which to work out is an important element to the overall benefits of every fitness regime. Clothing too should be unfussy and comfortable, to free your mind and allow you to maximise your breathing and movement techniques.

SUN POWER

The sun warms the earth and nurtures life, but as with everything else, balance is vital.

- **We need some sun to convert vitamin D in the body and create healthy bones and teeth.**
- **Research also shows that exposing the breasts to the sun may help combat breast cancer.**
- **However, as most of us are only too well aware, excess sun is harmful.**
- **High doses of intense sunlight can accelerate wrinkles and ageing and lead to skin cancer.**
- **If you have very pale skin that does not tan easily, you are far more vulnerable to the harmful effects of sun exposure.**
- **Treat the sun with respect by staying in the shade or covering up with clothes or a high SPF sun lotion, from 11am to 4pm.**
- **Sun causes damage by the release of free radicals which harm the body's immune mechanism; a diet in anti-oxidant nutrients (see Healthy Eating chapter) can help protect against this naturally.**

OXYGEN POWER FITNESS THERAPY (OPF)

Oxygen Power Fitness Therapy, devised by German physicist Professor Manfred von Ardenne, is a special breathing therapy which allows the body to utilise oxygen more efficiently. Chiva-Som's OPF programme lasts from one to three weeks and involves the following:

1. **Taking a mixture of minerals and vitamins to improve the body's ability to use oxygen.**
2. **Using normal breathing to enrich the blood with oxygen.**
3. **Undertaking a specially devised and medically supervised exercise and fitness programme designed to activate the circulation.**

Chiva-Som also offers a more intensive programme known as Oxygen Super Regeneration, OSR, which in addition to OPF includes oxygen ozone therapy or blood energising.

Rate of Perceived Exertion

Another easy way of checking exercise intensity is called the rate of perceived exertion or RPE. Ideally any exercise should feel 'somewhat hard' to 'very hard'. If it feels 'very hard' or 'very, very hard' you are exercising at too high an intensity and need to slow down a bit. If you feel the amount of effort you are putting in is 'very light' or 'very, very light' you are not exercising hard enough and should adjust your effort upwards.

To increase the rate of exertion, try using hand weights, always consulting a trained gym instructor first, to check the ideal weight for you.

If you have a sedentary job, the use of a multi-gym will help tone those infrequently used leg and arm muscles (right and far right).

Finding Your Target Heart Rate

A more scientific way of measuring exercise intensity is taking your pulse so as to find your target heart rate or THR.

For an athlete or someone who is very fit the THR will be around 85 per cent of their maximum heart rate or MHR – in other words the highest rate that her heart is capable of beating at. If you are reasonably fit, your THR should be

around 70 per cent of your MHR. If you are not so fit, your THR should be around 60 per cent of your MHR.

To work out your THR you need to know your estimated MHR, which you can work out by subtracting your age from 220.

eg If you are 30 years of age:

220 – 30 = 180

This gives you an MHR of 180 beats per minute.

To calculate your THR, multiply your MHR by the appropriate percentage for your level of fitness.

eg If you are a fit 30-year-old:

180 x 70% = 126

This means your THR would be 126 beats a minute when you are exercising.

If you are a less fit 30-year-old:

180 x 60% = 108

In this case, your THR would be 108 beats a minute when exercising.

SIX GOOD REASONS TO EXERCISE

1. **It helps the lungs and heart work more efficiently, increasing stamina.**
2. **It firms up the muscles and eliminates fat leading to a more streamlined appearance.**
3. **It boosts the immune system, making the body more resistant to disease.**
4. **It triggers the release of hormone-like brain chemicals called endorphins – natural antidotes to anger, depression, anxiety and stress.**
5. **It strengthens the heart and arteries so they are more efficient and can pump more blood with each beat.**
6. **It increases confidence and self-esteem, helps you withstand stress better and generally improves the quality of your life.**

Checking Your Pulse

To measure your heart rate:

- Find your pulse by placing your index and middle fingers on your wrist just below the thumb joint or in the groove of your neck.
- Press lightly and count the number of beats you feel in ten seconds. Then multiply this by six to get the number of beats per minute.
- When doing aerobic exercise, take your pulse around 3 to 5 minutes into your workout as you feel your heart rate begin to rise and you start breathing harder.
- If you are below your THR, push yourself a bit harder. If you are above your THR, decrease your effort. If you are on your THR, try to maintain the same level of effort.
- Check your THR at regular intervals throughout your workout.

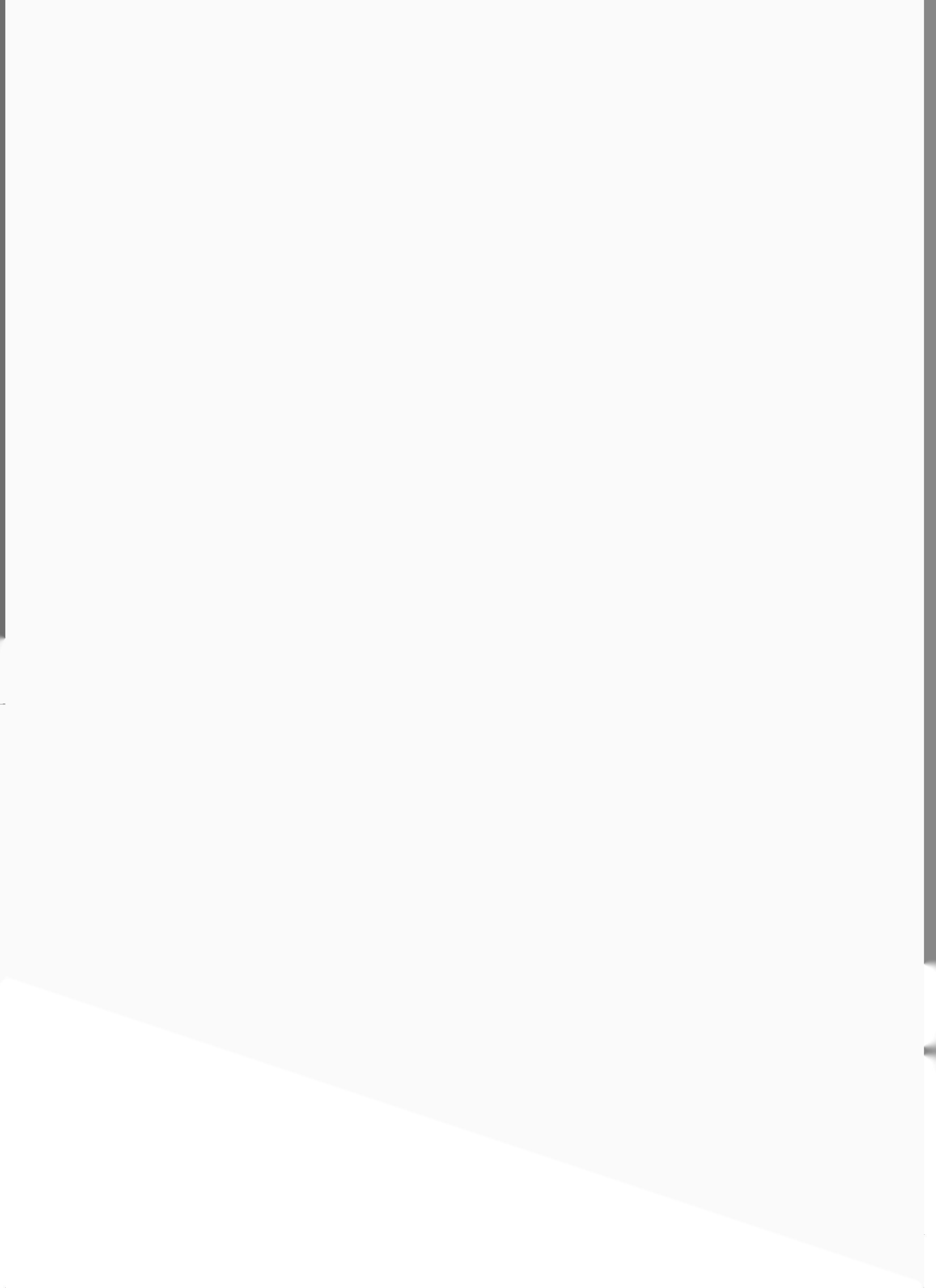

lives, stress has to be kept in balance. Some stress helps motivate us but when too many demands are made on us or stress is prolonged, it is damaging.

Pollution, anger and conflict at home or at work, processed food containing pesticides or additives, bad habits such as smoking and drinking both alcohol and caffeine, overeating, inactivity, diseases, infections and simply getting older are all 'negative stressors'. They increase our need for oxygen.

If this need is not met we enter a state of oxygen hunger which results in headaches, fatigue and lack of energy. Over the long term, exposure to negative stressors and oxygen deprivation can lead to chronic conditions such as premature ageing, furring and narrowing of the arteries, reduced lung capacity, stiff, creaking joints and spine. Stress is not discharged physically, and stress hormones continue to wash around the body, impeding our ability to rest and relax.

Ultimately your body has a reduced resistance to illness and lack of strength which can in turn make you prone to serious disease.

The good news is that there are ways of dealing with stress that can help us avoid this negative spiral.

Ten Ways to Beat Stress

1 Compensatory tactics. If you hit a bad patch at home or work, counterbalance it by putting energy into areas of your life that are under your control; for example, redecorate a room, do the garden, learn a new sport, improve your social life and have more fun.

2 Share the burden. Do not try to do everything yourself at home or work. Offload some of the work on to others so you get time to relax. You should also learn to say "No". You cannot expect to do everything and no-one should expect you to do so. If you find refusing difficult, try an assertiveness training course.

REFLEXOLOGY – HEALING THROUGH THE FEET

Reflexology, zone therapy or compression massage, has been used in India and China for 5,000 years. It works on the principle that the body's organs are mirrored in the feet. When an organ is diseased or not functioning properly, energy flowing down invisible channels or meridiens may become blocked or sluggish. This can cause crystals to form beneath the skin in the feet. By breaking down the crystals and rebalancing the flow of energy, health can be restored.

The therapy is used to relax the body, stimulate circulation and restore mental and physical harmony.

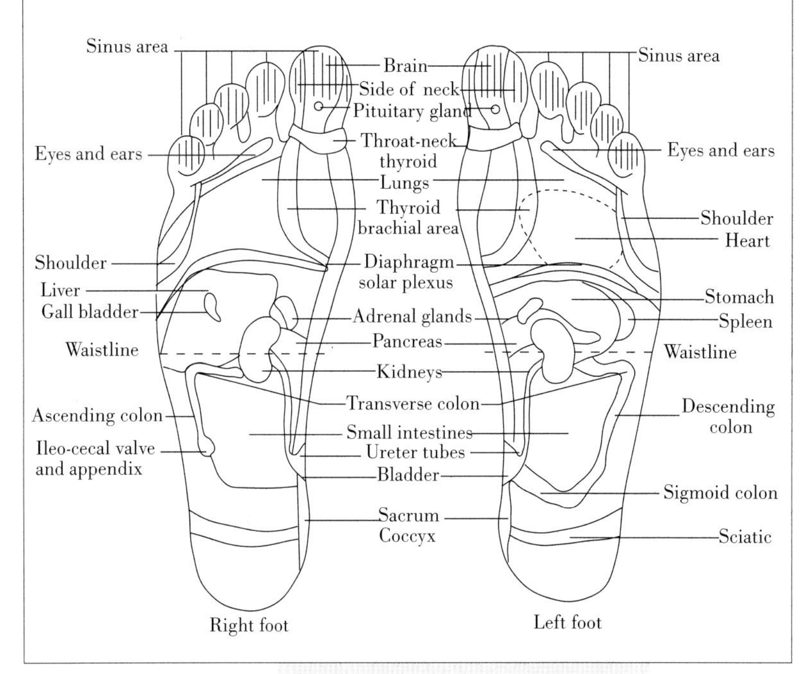

The diagram above shows how the feet mirror the organs of the body. By exerting pressure on the appropriate point a reflexology massage heals and rebalances.

Swimming combines fitness with fun, all year round.

3 Beat boredom. Boredom creates stress because our minds are unstimulated. Make an effort to seek out new experiences and challenges. Do not sit around waiting for things to happen – go out and do something.

4 Boost self-esteem. Periods of stress can cause a negative spiral of loss of confidence and self-doubt. Bolster confidence by reminding yourself of times when you have dealt successfully with problems in the past. Make a list of all your good qualities. Seek out friends who are positive and reassuring.

5 Plan to cope. Many potentially stressful situations can be anticipated in advance. Think about what problems may arise and plan ways to deal with them.

6 Know yourself. We sometimes deal less well with stress because of other things that are going on in our lives and our bodies. Use your knowledge of yourself and the way your body works to anticipate times when you may be less

able to cope with stress and try to make life easier on yourself – *eg* when you are suffering from jet-lag, when you have an especially heavy workload, or if you are a woman when you are pre-menstrual, pregnant or have just had a baby.

7 Take time out. When going through a period of stress it is vital to take some time off. Learn to relax and use simple relaxation and meditation techniques to enable you to switch off. Exercise is vital to discharge stress hormones and enable us to relax. It is especially important during a period of stress to fit in a daily walk, swim or other form of activity.

8 Sleep well. Sleep is vital when you are under stress to rest your body and mind.

9 Share problems. Under stress we are often tempted to draw in our horns and retreat from other people. Sharing problems can give you a new perspective and may offer new ways of solving them. Think about who you could call on when you are under stress. Poor communication can cause unnecessary stress, so work at improving your personal relationships.

10 Answer to yourself alone. Everyone enjoys the status of success. However, there may be a price to pay and only you can judge if it is too high. Consider where you are heading and why. Are you still trying to seek approval from your parents, your teachers, your peers? Remember the first person you should try to please is yourself.

Inner balance and mental well-being complement an outwardly healthy appearance.

EASING STRESS THE AROMATHERAPY WAY

The ancient art of aromatherapy is one of the most effective ways of dealing with stress. Our sense of smell is one of the most potent we possess. What we smell can affect how we feel. This is because aromas are processed by the limbic system in an ancient part of the brain which is linked to memory.

Humans in all parts of the world and throughout the ages have made use of scents to calm or invigorate. For instance, the Chinese have for centuries suspended balls of jasmine over the bed to clear the air and promote sweet dreams. Meanwhile the Victorians placed sachets of calming lavender in drawers and under pillows.

In aromatherapy, highly concentrated essential oils drawn from all parts of plants

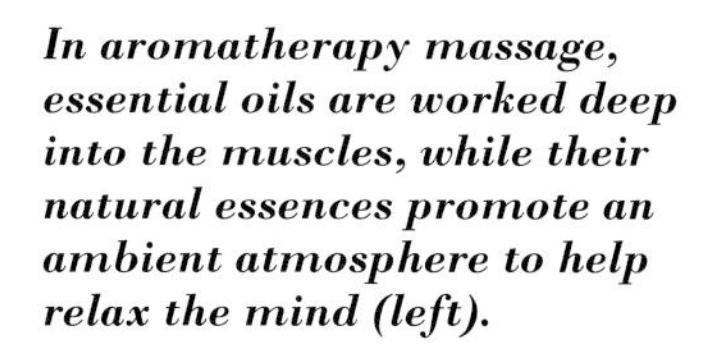

In aromatherapy massage, essential oils are worked deep into the muscles, while their natural essences promote an ambient atmosphere to help relax the mind (left).

AMBIENT AROMAS

AT WORK: Uplifting, stimulating and refreshing oils are the most useful oils for the workplace. Try basil, rosemary, bergamot, lemon and melissa.
REST: Relaxing and soothing oils are useful at home. Try rose, geranium, orange and lavender in the sitting-room. In the bedroom try rose, neroli (orange blossom) and lavender.

Oils can also be used to keep your home clean, healthy and free from insects.
AS DISINFECTANT: Use pine, lemon and tea tree on a damp cloth to disinfect the kitchen and bathroom. In the sick-room use bergamot, eucalyptus and juniper. As insect repellent use tea tree, eucalyptus, melissa, lemon grass or citronella.
FOR ENTERTAINING: Use oils to create the feel-good factor. Try clary, sage or jasmine. If you are having a party try orange, lemon grass, neroli (orange blossom). For a festive blend choose spicier oils such as frankincense, cedarwood, sandalwood, cinnamon and orange.

RECOMMENDED AROMATHERAPY OILS

OIL	PROPERTIES	USE FOR
Basil	Uplifting and refreshing	To ease stress and poor breathing
Bergamot	Uplifting, refreshing, relaxing, antiseptic	Sore throats
Cedarwood	Calming	Anxiety, coughs
Cinnamon	Warming	To create a good atmosphere. Note: Avoid in pregnancy
Frankincense	Relaxing, rejuvenating	Stress, skin problems
Geranium	Refreshing, relaxing, cleansing	To balance mind and body. Note: Avoid during first three months of pregnancy
Jasmine	Relaxing, soothing	Depression, emotionally healing
Juniper	Refreshing, relaxing and stimulating	Insomnia, arthritis, poor health
Lemon	Stimulating, antiseptic	Eases poor circulation and high blood pressure
Lemon grass	Toning, refreshing	Freshening rooms, deodorising, insect repellent
Melissa	Uplifting, refreshing	Easing tension and stress
Neroli (Orange blossom)	Calming, comforting	Panic, stress, insomnia
Orange	Sedative, balancing	Stress and depression
Rose	Emotionally healing, aphrodisiac	Easing guilt, grief, jealousy, balancing the heart, or for putting you in the mood for love
Rosemary	Invigorating, refreshing	A useful aid to concentration, for headaches or lifting mental fatigue
Sage	Stimulating, antiseptic	Helps ease tension, improves circulation
Sandalwood	Uplifting, aphrodisiac, tonic, antiseptic	Insect repellent, to lift spirits, skin problems, aphrodisiac
Tea tree	Antiseptic, cleansing	Insect repellent, to lift spirits, cure infections

are used to soothe and heal both body and mind. The oils can be used in a variety of ways: in massages, inhalations sprinkled on a handkerchief, in a room spray or in a special burner, added to the bath or used for compresses.

The Power of Sleep

A restful night's sleep is vital to allow the body to repair itself and the mind to recharge. All sorts of things can affect our ability to sleep. They include illness, humidity, storms, noise, an uncomfortable mattress, overindulgence in food or alcohol, overstimulating foods, as well as a whole range of emotional upsets such as loss or bereavement, quarrels with your partner, mental overload, depression, tension and sexual frustration.

Sleep disturbances may take the form of having trouble dropping off, waking up during sleep or waking up tired, oversleeping, disturbing dreams and nightmares, talking or walking in your sleep, snoring or sleep apnoea (when the sleeper temporarily stops breathing).

Ways to a More Restful Night

Good sleep begins in the daytime. Check your exercise routine and diet to make sure you are not overloading your body and are getting rid of stress hormones that can impede the ability to drop off. Take steps to resolve emotional difficulties such as problems with your partner, or loss. Share your problems with a friend, talk to a counsellor or seek an alternative therapy.

The ability to take time out for yourself in a calm environment can prove as restorative as many health or beauty regimes – the positive effect of Nature can be a permanent boost to the mind and spirit, as our intuitions relate to its rhythms and cycles.

Before you go to bed spend time winding down and avoid stimulants such as coffee, tea and alcohol. If you have specific worries write them down in a notebook and vow to deal with them the next day – then put it away and forget about them. Avoid stimulating films or other activities. Instead, do some yoga, meditation or breathing exercises to help you relax and wind down. A brisk walk can help ease away tension and make you feel pleasantly tired. Listen to a favourite (calming) piece of music or read a non-stimulating

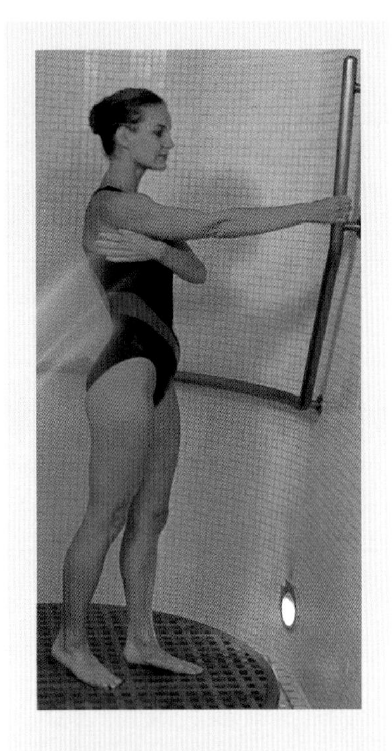

HYDROTHERAPY AT CHIVA-SOM

At Chiva-Som there is a whole range of spa treatments using water to choose from, all with benefits for health. Among them include:

- **Jacuzzi (37° centigrade). Stimulates and relaxes while increasing blood and lymphatic circulation.**
- **The Cool Plunge (27° centigrade). A step-down pool filled with cool water.**
- **Jet Shower Treatment (body temperature). A jet shower is aimed at the body in a stimulating deep massage that both relaxes and stimulates, helping to encourage the breakdown of fat and the drainage of toxins.**
- **Hydro Bath. The underwater massage with 180 jets helps eliminate fatty deposits. It also improves circulation and muscle toning.**
- **Flotation. A special saline solution, by providing a 'floating' sensation, induces deep mental relaxation, which reduces stress and tension.**

novel. Make your bedroom a calm, restful retreat – banish the TV, newspapers and anything else that detracts from the calm. If you are feeling very tense get up and get rid of some of your energy by taking a walk or doing something active.

Practise a breathing exercise, a meditation or visualisation. For instance, conjure up a beautiful scene and imagine yourself in it. Focus on sensual details, such as the feel of the sun on your skin, the waft of a warm breeze, the soft caress of water on your limbs. Breathe gently and slowly, making sure you are breathing from your abdomen and not your chest.

Keep a personal stereo by your bed and play a relaxation tape or a soothing piece of music.

Water – The Elixir of Life

Water is vital for life. As human beings we evolved from the sea and as individuals our first knowledge of the world is of being lapped by water deep in our mother's womb. Our bodies largely consist of water and each of our cells contains a mini-sea of minerals dissolved in water.

Seventy per cent of our earth's surface is covered by water. Most of this water is in the oceans from which life first emerged billions of years ago. The rest is frozen as ice or snow, flows in lakes, streams and rivers or is present in the atmosphere as rain, fog, mist, cloud or vapour. Humans have a special affinity with water and have always established settlements beside rivers or by the sea.

The oxygen we breathe in and the carbon dioxide we exhale dissolves in water in our bloodstream and is carried to and from each of our body cells and our lungs. Water helps keep our bodies at the right temperature and bathes and lubricates all our internal organs and joints. Without water we would be unable to digest the food we eat or excrete its waste. In other words, without water we would be unable to live.

On a practical basis water charts the body's life cycle; aesthetically it emanates vitality, symbolising the importance of balance and moderation (above and left).

Throughout the world water is associated with fertility and life. In Indian, Christian and African cultures, water is used to cleanse and purify body and mind and celebrate spiritual rebirth. In Hindu sacred scriptures, water is referred to as Matritamah – the most motherly. In Taoism, water stands for the strength of weakness and the fluidity of life as opposed to the hardness and rigidity of death. Think how the young, pliable branch of a tree with the vital sap of life running through it bends and sways in a strong wind but remains intact. An old, dried-up branch although it may be thicker and apparently stronger, is rigid and more liable to snap in a gale. In Buddhism, crossing the stream symbolises passing through the world of illusion to enlightenment.

Hydrotherapy – The Healing Power of Water

The power of water to soothe and heal has been recognised since time immemorial. Greek temples to the god of medicine, Asklepios, were often built at hot springs; steam baths were popular with the Romans and the Turks; the ancient Chinese and American-Indians both used water as therapy.

Water can be used to stimulate or relax, for exercising in or gently floating. Our bodies can benefit in several ways from water – we can drink it or apply it externally in a compress, as a wrap, or in spray form, we can immerse ourselves in it, in a bath, Jacuzzi or flotation tank, surround ourselves in its vapour and/or inhale it as steam.

Hydrotherapy, the use of water for therapy, has several benefits:

- It restores the body's natural cellular balance and drains away toxins.
- It stimulates blood and lymphatic circulation and encourages the flow of oxygen to the tissues, so helping to correct circulatory problems such as varicose veins, cramps and swelling.
- It is a useful part of a slimming package when combined with a low-calorie diet, exercise and a change in mental attitude.
- It helps prevent cardiovascular problems and fatigue.
- It relieves anxiety and stress.

Types of Hydrotherapy

Thermal therapies involve using hot water or steam to dilate blood vessels and lower blood pressure. This in turn encourages sweating which flushes out toxins, relaxes the muscles and joints and draws heat to the skin surface. When the water is moving and used to massage, it boosts circulation of the blood and lymphatic system, and both relaxes and stimulates the muscles.

Cryotherapies use cold water to constrict blood vessels causing blood pressure to rise, reduce inflammation and congestion and stimulate the flow of blood to internal organs. Cold water increases the rate of respiration and boosts the body's basal metabolic rate – the rate at which energy is burnt up. It increases the tone, energy and capacity of muscles and numbs nerve endings, helping to relieve pain.

Six Steps to Staying Healthy

1 Stay fit. Moderate activity such as walking or swimming for 30 minutes to an hour, three to four times a week should be enough to maintain a healthy heart and help combat other diseases, such as the brittle bone disease, osteoporosis that affects both men and women, and certain cancers such as testicular and breast cancer. Alternatively, do more vigorous aerobic exercise for at least 20 minutes, three times a week.

2 Watch your blood pressure. The systolic blood pressure – the upper figure of a blood pressure reading – is the pressure in your arteries when your heart contracts and pumps. The lower figure, the diastolic blood pressure is the pressure in the arteries when the heart muscle is relaxed and is refilling between beats. Ideally, your blood pressure should be 100-130 over 85 or lower. If it is 140/90 or higher, seek advice from a doctor.

3 Watch what you eat. In particular, avoid saturated fats found in meat, dairy foods and coconut. They push up levels of cholesterol in the body which is a risk factor for furring of the arteries.

IRIDOLOGY – THE EYES HAVE IT

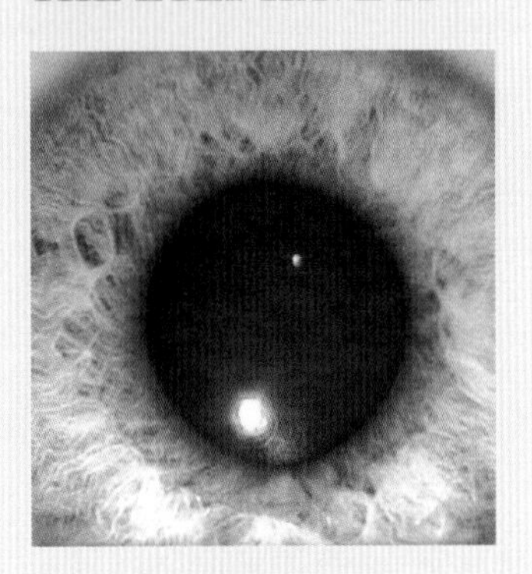

- **Poets have long seen eyes as the windows to the soul. In iridology, iris diagnosis, therapists analyse the iris to detect the health and well-being of your body. The state of your digestive system, circulation, cholesterol levels, levels of nutrients, areas of weakness and strength, and many other elements of health can be seen reflected in the eye.**
- **At Chiva-Som your eyes are analysed by a qualified iridologist/naturopath when you first come to visit, and again on departure, to show beneficial changes in your state of health which have been brought about by your stay at the spa.**
- **The diagram shows how iridology detects the health of each of the bodily parts, through the eyes.**

SKIN, LIMBS, MUSCLES, MOTOR NERVES
LIVER, SPLEEN, THYROID, ETC
BRAIN AND SEX ORGANS
LUNGS, BRONCHI, TRACHEA
HEART, PANCREAS, KIDNEYS
INTESTINES
STOMACH
1
2
3
4
5
6
7

Too many fats are also implicated in certain types of cancer, such as bowel cancer.

4 Don't smoke. Smoking is a major risk factor for high blood pressure, heart disease, lung cancer, bronchitis and a whole range of other life-threatening conditions. If you do smoke, take steps to stop.

5 Watch your stress levels. When we are stressed adrenalin is released which can cause the arteries to narrow. Although the precise links between stress and illness have yet to be unravelled, stress is associated with a number of common diseases including high blood pressure, heart disease, diabetes and cancer.

6 Know your family history. Draw up a family tree and where you can, mark in details of the various illnesses family members suffered from. Once you know what they are you can take steps to strengthen any potential areas of weakness, and avail yourself of any screening programmes designed to pick up early signs of serious diseases.

The holistic approach to well-being is simple; it is to address the needs of mind, body, and spirit, through exercise, relaxation and diet.

Staying Healthy and Avoiding Diseases

Everyone suffers minor ailments from time to time. They are your body's way of ridding itself of toxins and re-establishing a state of balance. However, sometimes the accumulated effects of too much stress, ageing or the genetic blueprint you inherited from your family can render you more vulnerable to serious disease. High blood pressure, raised cholesterol levels, the inability to deal with sugar (insulin resistance), diabetes, rheumatoid arthritis and certain cancers all run in families.

Conventional drugs can have harsh side-effects and in some cases can be far more dangerous than the illnesses they are used to treat. Alternative therapies can help you stay healthy so you are less likely to fall sick. Most minor illnesses can be treated quite simply using alternative therapies and remedies like those highlighted throughout this chapter.

If your body has broken down more seriously, however, and you have developed a condition such as heart disease, you will need treatment from a conventional doctor. In this case, alternative therapies and remedies can be used to support your body and help you withstand the effects of orthodox treatment.

HEALTHY EATING

A Holistic Approach to Eating

The expression, 'You are what you eat' is used so often that it has become a cliché. Nevertheless it is still true that the quality of the food you put into your body is one of the key elements of a long, healthy life.

Our bodies need high quality, nutritious food to provide the cells with the nutrients they need, to give us the energy to get through each day, and keep our bodies healthy and young. What you eat is ultimately reflected in the health of your hair, nails, teeth, skin and body shape as well as the way you feel mentally.

A healthy diet contains all the vitamins, minerals and other nutrients needed by your cells and is balanced so that it provides the exact amount of energy you need to live. The rules of good eating and following a holistic approach are very simple.

A regular diet of wholegrains helps combat cholesterol (below), and has a positive cleansing effect on the body. The cup of life: a diet of fresh and unrefined foods is recommended (right), especially where slimming is the aim and clearer skin the gain.

Eating for Life

Life-giving food is as fresh and as close to its natural state as possible. In traditional cultures people cultivate their own food which means that fruit, vegetables and so on are eaten straight after being harvested. In industrialised societies, food has often been transported and stored, sometimes for many weeks, before it reaches the shop, let alone our plates. In the process it loses many nutrients. As it deteriorates, free radicals – harmful molecules that damage cells – are produced by a process known as oxidation.

The second rule of good eating is that food should be natural and whole. Food in its whole state contains a full complement of nutrients. For example, wholegrains contain

OZS CUPS

LEMON ZEST

Lemons help improve and support good liver and gall bladder functions. A dash of freshly squeezed lemon or lime taken in hot water every day will stimulate gastric juices and cleanse the digestive system. It is especially good if you are trying to lose weight as it helps break down fat and reduces appetite. Lemons and limes are also high in vitamins A and C, calcium, which is vital for healthy bones and teeth, and phosphorus which helps improve brain power and is known as 'the beauty mineral'.

Start the day in a calm and restful environment (above); where and how you eat is as important for effective digestion as what you actually choose to eat. Water is the crucial companion to a balanced diet (far right).

fibre which helps protect against the accumulation of cholesterol and cleanses the bowel of toxic chemicals that have been linked to bowel cancer.

Food that has been sprayed with chemicals or had additives or preservatives added, enable them to stay fresh-looking longer, and fills our bodies with poisons. Food that has been altered by refining or processing is stripped of protective nutrients that help to keep us healthy and protect our bodies against a whole host of diseases, including cancer and heart disease.

Food that is whole and fresh needs little cooking and this brings us to another rule of healthy eating, that food should only be cooked lightly, if at all. It is recommended that one raw meal of salad, vegetables or fruit should be eaten each day.

Raw and lightly cooked foods are high in nutrients which help nourish the cells, ensuring they are healthy. They also help cleanse the cells and encourage them to eliminate toxins and stored wastes. Our cells contain the genetic blueprint that we inherit from our parents, so a nutritious diet is vital to ensure that our children and our children's children are healthy.

Cooking, on the other hand, destroys more life-giving nutrients and some methods of cooking such as frying, barbecuing and any other method that involves charring food, releases cancer-causing chemicals. Cooked food places a negative stress on the digestive system because it is devoid of live enzymes. The best methods of cooking are steaming, baking, grilling and stir-frying, all of which preserve nutrients in food.

Balance is a key element of holistic living and can be applied to eating as much as to every other area of life. In terms of food, a healthy balance involves eating a variety of foods. Eating too much of any one sort of food creates an imbalance in the system. Buffet-style meals that allow you to combine a variety of different foods are one way of ensuring you get all the essential nutrients needed for health.

Balance also applies to the overall amount of food you eat. Moderation is the key to a healthy, clean body. Eating too much overloads the cells and forces the body to use vital energy in digestion. Most of us could benefit from decreasing our calorie intake. Your aims should be to consume just the right amount depending on your activity level (see page 36 to work out exactly how many calories you need).

Just as important as what you eat in the holistic approach to eating is how you eat. Rushing home from a busy day at work and immediately sitting down to eat, snacking in front of the TV, eating too fast, shovelling down food while reading the newspaper, thinking about the next meeting you have to go to or getting into an argument over the dinner table, all trigger the release of stress hormones into your blood stream. These in turn upset your digestive system so food is not digested or eliminated properly, and encourages fat to be converted into cholesterol which contributes to the furring of the arteries, and which can ultimately lead to heart disease.

The best way to take your meals is in a calm, quiet environment. Try to savour each mouthful, and really focus on what you are eating, taking the time to taste it properly, to feel its texture, to chew, swallow and pause before taking another mouthful. Eating slowly will also help you regulate the amount you eat.

Water and Eating

As we saw in the last chapter, our bodies are made up of 70 per cent of water and water is especially important in relation to food and eating. Water is vital to enable us to digest our food, to absorb it, to transport nutrients to the body's cells and tissues including the lungs and the bloodstream, and to excrete the

CHIVA-SOM'S TEN RULES FOR HEALTHY EATING

1. **Eat food that is whole.**
2. **Eat food that is fresh and 'alive'.**
3. **Eat food raw or only cooked lightly – steamed, grilled or baked.**
4. **Eat food that is pure and non-toxic.**
5. **Eat a variety of foods.**
6. **Eat the right amount of calories.**
7. **Drink six to ten glasses of pure spring water a day. The amount depends on the climate you live in and the amount of exercise you get.**
8. **Eat three meals a day, taking your last meal at least three hours before bedtime.**
9. **Eat slowly and chew your food well.**
10. **Eat in a calm, quiet atmosphere.**

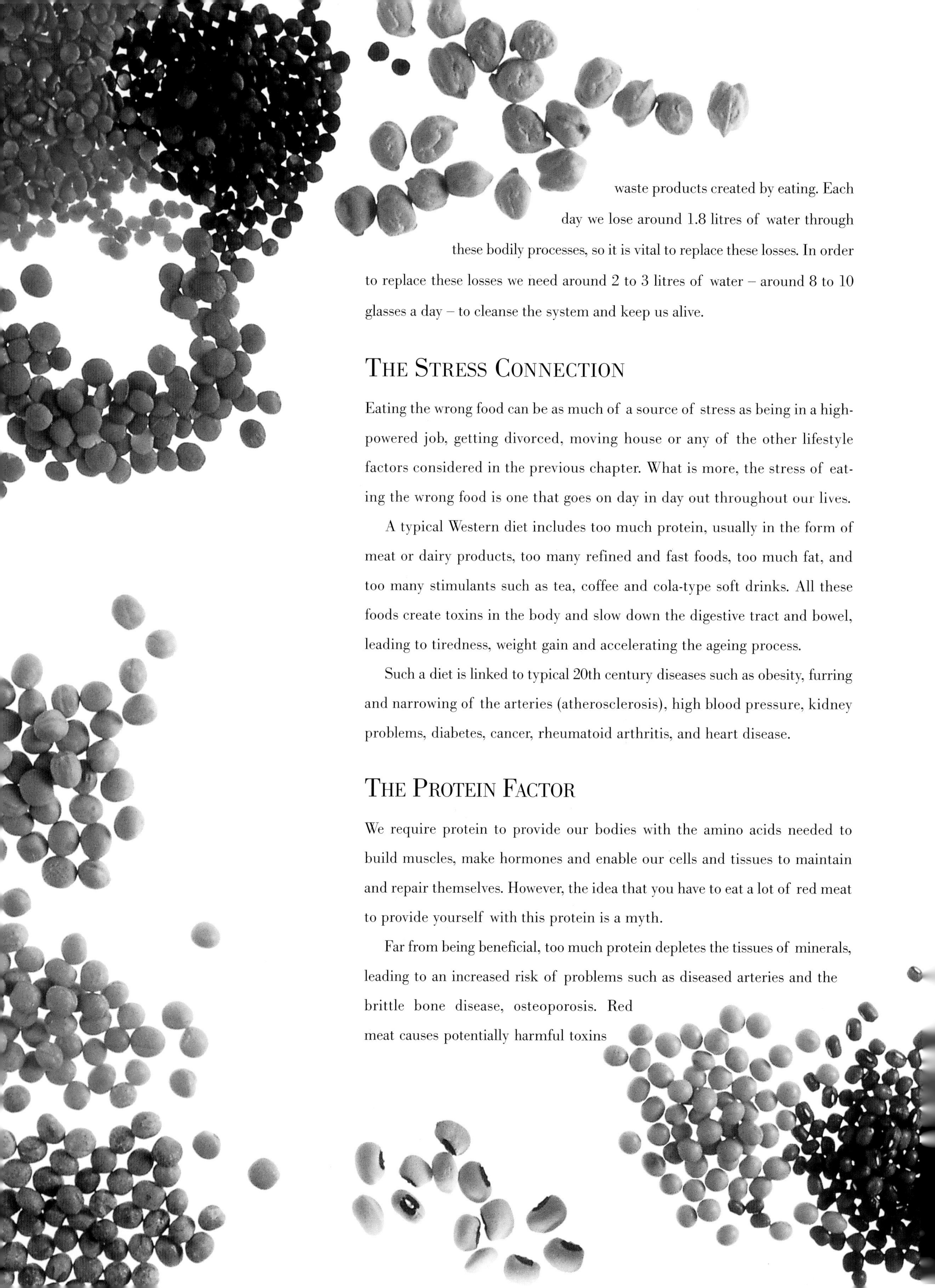

waste products created by eating. Each day we lose around 1.8 litres of water through these bodily processes, so it is vital to replace these losses. In order to replace these losses we need around 2 to 3 litres of water – around 8 to 10 glasses a day – to cleanse the system and keep us alive.

The Stress Connection

Eating the wrong food can be as much of a source of stress as being in a high-powered job, getting divorced, moving house or any of the other lifestyle factors considered in the previous chapter. What is more, the stress of eating the wrong food is one that goes on day in day out throughout our lives.

A typical Western diet includes too much protein, usually in the form of meat or dairy products, too many refined and fast foods, too much fat, and too many stimulants such as tea, coffee and cola-type soft drinks. All these foods create toxins in the body and slow down the digestive tract and bowel, leading to tiredness, weight gain and accelerating the ageing process.

Such a diet is linked to typical 20th century diseases such as obesity, furring and narrowing of the arteries (atherosclerosis), high blood pressure, kidney problems, diabetes, cancer, rheumatoid arthritis, and heart disease.

The Protein Factor

We require protein to provide our bodies with the amino acids needed to build muscles, make hormones and enable our cells and tissues to maintain and repair themselves. However, the idea that you have to eat a lot of red meat to provide yourself with this protein is a myth.

Far from being beneficial, too much protein depletes the tissues of minerals, leading to an increased risk of problems such as diseased arteries and the brittle bone disease, osteoporosis. Red meat causes potentially harmful toxins to form in the bowel and is associated with kidney problems, high blood pressure and certain sorts of cancer such as bowel cancer.

In fact we can get most or all of the amino acids our bodies need from a balanced diet of fruits, vegetables, pulses, nuts, seeds and wholegrains. These are easier to absorb and place less stress on the system than red meat. A bowl of lentils with a flat bread made of whole wheat or millet or rice, for example, will provide you with all the amino acids you need without the fat you would get from tucking into a plate of steak and French fries. Occasional lean, white meat, fish or game if you like it is fine, but try not to exceed 50 to 80 grammes a day.

Stock Up on Starch

Another myth that needs demolishing is that too much starchy food is bad for you. This is certainly true if the starch is the refined sort found in biscuits, pastries, white flour and sweets. Such foods flood the bloodstream with sugar, which is soon burnt up (see previous chapter) leading to peaks and troughs of energy and mood. These surges of blood sugar put the pancreas under stress, leading to a condition known as insulin resistance which is involved in both diabetes and heart disease. Refined sugar also leaches the body of B-complex vitamins which are needed for a healthy nervous system and to help combat stress.

Unrefined starches, or complex carbohydrates in the form of wholegrains, pulses, vegetables and fruit by contrast take the body some time to digest but the nutrients in them are easily absorbed, so they provide steady levels of energy and avoid highs and lows of mood. What is more, people who eat lots of starchy, fibrous foods including vegetables and fruit have a lower risk of both heart disease and bowel cancer.

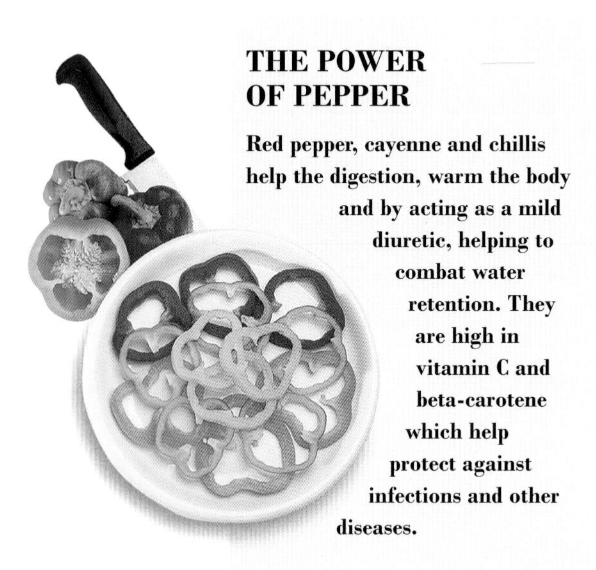

THE POWER OF PEPPER

Red pepper, cayenne and chillis help the digestion, warm the body and by acting as a mild diuretic, helping to combat water retention. They are high in vitamin C and beta-carotene which help protect against infections and other diseases.

UNZIP A BANANA

Bananas are high in biotin which is vital in slimming. They also help improve memory, cleanse the body, regulate heartbeat, maintain healthy skin and eyes, ease period pains, prevent baldness and help you to sleep better.

Bananas are slightly higher in calories than other fruits and those on a weight-loss programme should eat them in moderation.

Raw to the core: fruits and vegetables and the vitamins and minerals stored in them are the artillery against disease, infection and ageing (right and far right).

Fibre, especially the gluey soluble type found in pulses such as lentils, fruit such as apples, pears and cereals like rye, barley and oats reduce cholesterol levels. Starchy foods also act as fuel for bacteria in the bowel and release chemicals that are protective against cancer. Starchy foods also slow the rate of cell division and hence reduce the risk of potentially cancerous cells.

Good Fats and Bad Fats

People in the West consume almost half of their diet as fat. Experts such as US age researcher Roy Walford argue that between ages 30 and 50 we need consume only 10 to 15 per cent of calories as fat. However for many people in the West, fats make up almost half of their diet. This is a clear source of imbalance. Too much fat is linked to high levels of 'bad' cholesterol in the blood, especially when it is the saturated type found in animal and dairy products, which contributes to furring and narrowing of the arteries.

True, our bodies do need a small amount of fat to provide the cells with essential fatty acids which are needed for repair and maintenance. Vitamin E, found in nuts and seeds, which helps protect against heart disease for instance is fat soluble. Beta-carotene, another important vitamin found in red, orange and yellow fruits and vegetables, is better used by the body in the presence of fat.

However, it is vital that it is the right kind of fat. The best sources are green leafy vegetables which contain linolenic acid which is converted by the body into beneficial fatty acids; oily fish (mackerel, cod, salmon, tuna, sardines), which contain omega-3 fatty acids which help combat furring of the arteries, and nuts and seeds, and oils from nuts, seeds and fruits such as olive oil, flaxseed, linseed, mustard and sesame seed oils.

Fabulous Fruits and Vital Vegetables

Seasonal fruits are an essential part of a healthy balanced diet. Fruit is easily digested and cleansing. It has a cooling, calming action on the body and helps to reduce stress. Fruit has a high water content. It also contains fruit sugars which help provide the body with energy.

Vegetables are the other hinge of a healthy diet. They are a vital source of fibre, starch, vitamins and minerals. Like fruit they are low in fat, although they are a source of linolenic acid which is needed by the body to create healthy fatty acids. And, as vegetable fibre is not used as energy, vegetables are lower in calories than fruit.

Both fruit and vegetables are important sources of anti-oxidant vitamins and minerals which help zap free radicals – harmful molecules that damage cells and cause premature ageing and conditions such as cancer, heart disease, rheumatoid arthritis, diabetes, cataracts and the eye disease, macular degeneration.

Vitamin C, found in all fruit, is especially important because it helps combat a whole range of infections and conditions, from the common cold to heart disease. Vitamin E, a fat soluble vitamin, has been found to protect the arteries and helps combat heart disease.

Another vital vitamin is beta-carotene, which is converted in the body into vitamin A, and which is found in red, orange and yellow fruits such as mangoes, papayas, carrots, sweet potatoes, squash, pumpkin and cantaloupe melons. This and other carotenes are especially important in combating cancer, heart disease and other degenerative diseases of ageing.

EAT TO BEAT STRESS

At Chiva-Som you will learn a new way of eating that helps reduce stress levels to help ensure that life is more relaxing and manageable in the future.

GO FOR

- **Potassium-rich foods such as asparagus, carrots, corn, spinach, tomatoes, cantaloupes, plums, strawberries, apples, fish, cod, salmon and tuna**
- **Foods rich in vitamins such as green vegetables, millet, brown rice, wild rice, oats, chickpeas, lentils, Brewer's yeast and legumes**
- **Foods high in vitamins A and C such as apricots, mangoes, broccoli, lettuces, papayas, prunes, limes, lemons, pumpkin and peppers of all kinds**
- **Calcium-rich foods such as cabbage, spinach, parsley,**

broccoli, lettuces, onions, sesame and sunflower seeds and fish
- **Foods high in zinc such as pumpkin seeds, mushrooms, brown rice, sesame seeds, Brewer's yeast and seafood**
- **Foods high in magnesium and iron such as green leafy vegetables, parsley, fish, cashew nuts, cabbage and beans.**

Chiva-Som also recommends taking a good B-complex vitamin supplement or 2-3 teaspoons of Brewer's yeast each day.

A FINE BALANCE

At Chiva-Som you will learn that a healthy diet is all about balance. Consult the following lists to discover how to attain a healthy balance by eating more of some foods and less of others:

CONSUME MORE

- **Fruit and vegetables**
- **Wholegrains *eg* rice, millet, oats, wholewheat**
- **Fibrous foods (fruit, vegetables, wholegrains)**
- **Chemical-free white meat such as chicken**
- **Fish and seafood**
- **Pure spring water**
- **Herbal teas and decaffeinated coffee, soda water, lemon juice, clear soup**
- **Soya milk, low-fat natural yoghurt, skimmed or low-fat milk, low-fat cheese, cottage cheese**
- **Lemon juice, apple cider vinegar, herbs, spices, low-salt stock cubes**

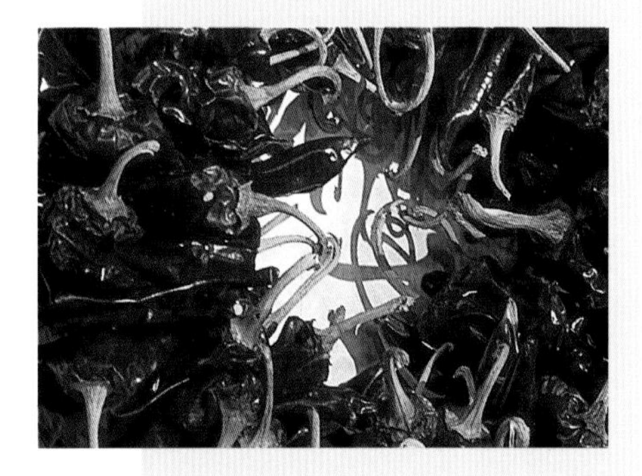

CONSUME LESS

- **Processed and refined foods, foods containing saturated fat and refined sugar**
- **Full fat dairy produce such as cheese, milk and cream**
- **Refined, sugary foods such as biscuits, chocolate, chips**
- **Avoid red meats**
- **Smoked and processed meats**
- **Coffee, tea, cola-type soft drinks, alcohol, liqueurs**
- **Table salt, stock cubes, bottled sauces**

Salt of the Earth

Minerals found in food are essential to life but the typical Western diet contains an imbalance of one particular mineral; sodium or salt. This is partly because of adding extra salt to food in cooking or at the table, and partly because high levels of salt are used as a preservative and taste stimulant in processed food. A high level of salt or sodium is the chief culprit in the development of high blood pressure, which is why it is important to cut down on the salt you consume by avoiding processed, refined foods and stopping adding salt to food at the table. It is better to flavour foods with herbs and spices than to add extra salt. Natural salt is found in abundance in foods such as celery, lettuce, dandelion, cabbage and kelp.

When you are active and perspiring a lot, you lose salt in sweat. However, it is never necessary to take extra salt in tablet form. You should be aware that when you sweat a lot, you lose more water than salt so the most important thing to do is to drink more water to counteract this loss and restore your body's balance.

Eating the Right Amount

The exact amount you need to eat each day will depend on both your metabolism and your activity levels. To work out how many calories you need a day multiply your ideal body weight in kilogrammes by the following number of calories, depending on your lifestyle:

Your job is sedentary and you get little exercise	30 calories
Your job is sedentary but you get some light exercise	35 calories
Your job involves some activity and you also get some moderate exercise	40 calories
You have an active job and/or also get plenty of exercise	45 calories

So, if you are a man weighing 70 kgs and have moderate levels of activity you would need 2,800 calories a day. If you are a woman weighing 50 kgs and do some light exercise you would need 1,750 calories a day.

Eating to Lose Weight

Excess weight is a factor in high blood pressure, furring of the arteries, diabetes, premature ageing and certain sorts of cancer, such as breast cancer. The dietary principles outlined above should help you lose weight if you need to do so as well. However, it can help to have a more structured plan for weight loss.

Like everything else, your weight is all a matter of balance. If you consume more calories than you need you will gain weight; if you consume fewer you will lose weight. To lose a pound of fat a week therefore you need to reduce your calorie intake by 500 a day or 3,500 a week. You can use the equation on the previous page to help you decide how many calories you need to consume in order to start shedding that solid flesh.

Some foods are more calorific than others, while others are more easily laid down as fat: fatty foods and alcohol for example are more likely to pile on the pounds than fruit and vegetables because of the way they are processed by the body.

However, calories are not the whole story. There is an emotional aspect to food. Changing your attitudes to food is important too. Overweight people have been found to eat in a different way to people of normal weight. They tend to eat and drink too much at night, eat quickly, snack often, use eating and drinking as a way of dealing with stress, are more easily tempted by the look and smell of food and feel unable to say "No" when faced with food. If you are not happy with your life, are over-stressed or are hanging on to emotional baggage from your past, it is harder to lose weight.

A SAMPLE DAY'S MENU

ON RISING:
A glass of hot water with a dash of lemon or lime to detoxify and cleanse the liver and digestive system.

BREAKFAST:
One or two pieces of fruit or a starch *eg* puffed rice, rye flakes, corn flakes or oatmeal with skimmed milk, soya milk or nut milk.

MID-MORNING:
A piece of fruit *eg* berries, pears, apples, melons, pineapple, grape-fruit, papaya.

LUNCH:
Protein *eg* steamed fish, skinned chicken, tofu etc; vegetables raw or steamed. Fresh salad with four or five different vegetables.

MID-AFTERNOON:
A piece of fruit or vegetable or freshly pressed vegetable or fruit juice, diluted with pure water *eg* watermelon, carrot, celery, pineapple, grapefruit or apple juice.

DINNER:
Protein with vegetables.

Note: Remember to keep your total protein intake at no more than 50 to 80 grammes a day.

With a well-adjusted diet and exercise regime to match, you will find it less of a strain keeping your preferred body-shape.

SLIMMING CHOICES

Choose from:

VEGETABLES: asparagus, alfalfa, celery, cucumbers, radishes, spinach, bamboo shoots, broccoli, beans, bean sprouts, Brussels sprouts, cauliflower, cabbage, carrots, lettuce, morning glory, mushrooms, onions, peppers, pumpkin, tomatoes, turnips, okra, courgettes (zucchini), kale, palm hearts.

FRUIT: apples, pineapple, papaya, pomelo, blackberries, rose apple, guava, watermelon, mango, blackcurrants, strawberries, rhubarb, loganberries, blueberries, lemons, limes.

PROTEIN: fish, pulses and wholegrains should be the main protein; meat should be lean and skinned; dairy foods should be low fat *eg* skimmed milk, cottage cheese, low-fat yoghurt. Only one of the above should be eaten at the main meal.

EAT IN MODERATION: apricots, bananas, avocados, peaches, oranges, nuts, greengages, olives.

The time and effort taken to prepare and present food, is part of the enjoyment and appreciation of the meals we eat at home (right).

The goodness found in many nuts and seeds (top right) is further complemented by their multiple uses in cooking.

Eating at Home

An everyday diet should be practical, varied and easy to prepare. Eating three small meals a day ensures you get all the nutrients you need and helps to maintain steady energy levels. It is best to avoid nibbling between meals, but if you must have a snack, go for a piece of fruit, some carrot, celery or cucumber sticks or, if you are not watching your weight, a mix of sunflower and pumpkin seeds and some dried fruits.

Eating Out

In the past it was sometimes hard to avoid rich, fatty, heavy meals when eating out. Today, with so many restaurants serving more health conscious menus, it is much easier to stick to the principles of healthy eating. It is all a matter of making sensible choices from the menu.

For starters go for clear soups or consommés, tomato juice, melon, grapefruit or fruit cocktails, oysters, salad without mayonnaise, or smoked salmon. If you are served with bread or bread sticks you can eat them as part of your overall meal, but avoid the butter that comes with them.

For main courses choose fish, chicken, turkey, veal, venison or game, preferably grilled. Avoid anything that comes in cream-based or fatty sauce. Order a good

portion of vegetables or salad. Choose raw or steamed vegetables and ask that butter and rich sauces are left off. Avoid fried or roast potatoes, fried rice and pastas in creamy sauces. If you still feel hungry go for fresh fruit, fresh fruit salad, sorbet or a low-fat yoghurt as dessert, but do not feel that you have to have a third course if you have eaten enough. Buffets are a good way to combine all the necessary nutrients.

Eating for a Long, Healthy Life

Eating in the way outlined will not only ensure that you stay slim and fit, it may also help you to live longer. The science of ageing has progressed by leaps and bounds over the past few years. We now have enough knowledge to ensure that staying healthy, young and fit to between 100 and 110 years is not an impossible dream.

It is not known exactly why people age. However, one of the most convincing theories is that it is a result of attack by free radicals – harmful molecules

EAT TO BEAT AGEING

As well as the healthy eating recommendations already outlined, Chiva-Som recommends the following practices as part of an anti-ageing programme:

- **Periods of detoxification or cleansing to balance and rest the body's systems, enhance elimination and improve digestion.**
- **Taking food supplements designed to combat the ageing process.**
- **Using anti-ageing herbs.**

HERBS FOR LONGEVITY

These include garlic which is anti-viral, anti-fungal, anti-bacterial and helps combat both cancer and heart disease; ginseng, a well-known longevity herb which supports the adrenals and the

immune system; cayenne, to stimulate circulation and elimination, lower blood pressure and cholesterol; gotu kola, which helps improve memory, reduces fluid retention and acts as a glandular tonic.

CARDIO-PROTECTION ON YOUR PLATE

Make sure you get a good supply of the following:

VITAMIN C-RICH FOODS: guava, capsicum, blackcurrants, parsley, broccoli, lemon, lychees, cantaloupe melon, okra and lettuce.

VITAMIN E: sesame seeds, millet, cucumber, peas, Brussels sprouts, apples, bananas, carrots, celery, lotus root and lettuce.

GOOD OILS: linseed, sunflower, wheatgerm and olive.

FIBRE: found in cereals, especially oats, pulses and the skins of fruit and vegetables.

SUPPLEMENTS: take 1-3 teaspoons of lecithin granules.

FOOD SUPPLEMENTS FOR LIFE

Chiva-Som has produced its own complete food supplement. The first bio-natural food supplement in the world produced according to the humanitics formula, it consists of vitamins, minerals, anti-oxidants and phyto-nutrients in exact quantities for optimal health. The product is made from the finest natural herbal ingredients from around the world, using advanced pharmaceutical techniques.

Consisting of just two types of pills, one contains water soluble vitamins and minerals, while the other has fat soluble vitamins and other minerals. One is taken in the morning and the other in the evening. Together they provide the body with a balanced combination in an optimal dosage.

The food supplement combination helps to lower cholesterol, prevent premature ageing, optimise physical and mental energy and control weight.

that attack cell membranes and tissues. Free radicals are known to be involved in heart disease, cancer, diabetes and cataracts – to name just a few. Some major sources of free radicals are cigarettes, sunlight, X-rays, fried foods, radiation, air pollution, pesticides, anaesthetics, prescribed and non-prescription drugs, solvents, alcohol and stress.

A good supply of anti-oxidant vitamins and minerals, in particular vitamins A, E, C, beta-carotene, and the trace element selenium, are vital to protect against free radical damage; nutrients, which as we have seen are available in abundance in fruit, vegetables, cereals, nuts and seeds.

Another theory of ageing is that it is a result of stagnation within the circulation, digestive tract and bowels. Intriguingly, this theory too relates to what we eat and the way we eat. Good colon function, brought about by eating wholesome nutritious food, good digestion, assimilation and elimination, together with regular exercise to stimulate energy and circulation and maintaining a positive attitude, all help support vitality and circulation and combat stagnation.

Another factor in longevity may be calorie restriction. Numerous studies have shown that the longest lived people of the world, such as the Hunzas who live in the Himalayas, eat a low-calorie diet. Meanwhile, those who have the lowest life expectancy live on diets high in animal fats and proteins.

Eating for a Healthy Heart

Heart disease is the biggest killer in the Western world. Both risk factors for heart disease, such as raised cholesterol levels and high blood pressure and the manifestations of heart disease *ie* furring of the arteries (atherosclerosis) and heart attacks, are closely linked to what we eat.

Reducing the Risks

Cholesterol is manufactured in the liver and some is needed for the health of cell membranes and to help the body manufacture bile, needed for digestion and other hormones. However, too much cholesterol is harmful.

To balance cholesterol levels you should avoid eating too many foods rich in fat, such as butter, hard cheese and meat, and foods rich in cholesterol, such as egg yolks, mayonnaise, liver, patés, prawns, scallops and crabs.

At the same time you should increase foods that actively lower cholesterol.

SPRING CLEAN YOUR SYSTEM

ORGAN	DETOX ENCOURAGERS	FOODS FOR THOUGHT	SUPPLEMENTARY BENEFITS
Lungs	Deep breathing, yoga, t'ai chi, aerobic exercise	Lotus root, ginger, fenugreek, fresh fish, horseradish, garlic, lobelia	Calcium phosphate, magnesium, Co-Q10, zinc, essential fatty acids
Skin	Dry skin brushing, sauna, swimming, hydrotherapy, Epsom salts	Oats, fresh fish, pumpkin seeds, sunflower seeds, green leafy vegetables, papaya, carrots, root vegetables, barley, horsetail, wholegrains, apricots, tofu, dates, figs, good oils, lettuce, avocado	Ginger, garlic, cayenne, vitamins A, B, D, zinc, silica, iron, essential fatty acids
Kidneys	Increased water intake; juices: cucumber, parsley, celery; dandelion coffee, watermelon-seed tea, cranberry juice, mullein tea, potassium broth, barley water	Watermelon, celery, cucumber, garlic, asparagus, parsley, watercress, horseradish, raw honey, goat's milk, apples, pears, mangoes, papaya, potato skin	Vitamin B6, vitamin K, magnesium, sodium sulphate
Bowels	Massage, enemas	Dried dates, prunes, bentonite powder (volcanic ash); colonic irrigation; water with slippery elm and psyllium husks	Fibre-rich foods, figs, peaches, pears, green leafy vegetables, wholegrains, lacto-baccillus acidophillus, papain, bromelain, fibre, hydrochloric acid
Liver	Beet juice, water with lemon, apple juice, dandelion coffee/tea	Dandelion leaves, asparagus, radish, beetroot, grapefruit, olive oil, lemon juice, endive, watercress	Dandelion, B vitamins, vitamin C, methionine, folic acid, vitamin B12, choline

10 SLIMMING WAYS

1. **Learn to label watch: many foods contain hidden fat and sugar.**
2. **Present meals attractively by garnishing with lemon wedges, parsley, watercress or other fresh herbs.**
3. **Use smaller plates to make meals look larger.**
4. **Don't buy high-calorie snacks – then you won't be tempted.**
5. **Use apple concentrate as a sugar substitute in salads.**
6. **When stir-frying use vegetable stock instead of oil.**

7. **The colour green is an appetite suppressant.**
8. **Use baking as an alternative to deep-frying.**
9. **Remember to eat slowly.**
10. **Once you have reached your target weight, continue to eat according to healthy eating principles. However, you can allow yourself a treat once a week.**

Weigh it up for yourself: the mind and body can be regularly serviced with a balanced diet of seasonal fresh fruit and raw vegetables.

CHIVA-SOM'S CLEANSING DIET

This is a medically supervised programme which involves:

- **A three-day diet including a combination of cleansing cocktails of fruit and vegetable juices, consommés and herbal teas.**
- **On the third day raw fresh salads, steamed vegetables and a fruit compote are included as a preparation for resuming normal eating.**
- **A variety of supplements designed to speed up detoxification and the elimination of wastes are prescribed.**
- **Treatments to support the cleansing actions of the dietary regime include: aromatherapy, Swedish massage, mud treatments and body masks.**
- **You are also encouraged to take light exercise such as t'ai chi, yoga, stretch, aqua-aerobics, light swimming or walking.**

These include garlic, onion, ginger, natural yoghurt and alfalfa.

High blood pressure is another strong risk factor for heart disease. One of its main causes is an imbalance in sodium (salt) and other minerals including magnesium, calcium, manganese and potassium. At the same time as reducing your intake of salt you should increase your intake of foods rich in these minerals, such as berries, guava, spinach, kelp, pecans, barley, lima beans, bananas, citrus fruits, sardines, herrings, avocado, raisins and dates.

Blood pressure is also closely linked to the emotions, so calming B-vitamins, found in millet, sesame seeds, soya beans, wholegrains, walnuts and soya beans can be helpful.

Both furring of the arteries and heart attacks, the two main signs of heart disease, are a result of an imbalance in the body's oxygen balancing mechanism.

Free radicals – rogue molecules that damage cells caused by oxidation – are involved both in creating the fatty streaks that lead to furring of the arteries and in damaging the heart's muscle cells when they are deprived of oxygen during a heart attack.

Combating the Manifestations of Heart Disease

A diet high in vitamins A, C and E, and a supplement called co-enzyme Q10 is recommended. Starchy, carbohydrate foods also help to protect against heart attacks.

Eating a diet high in these nutrients can be cardio-protective if you have a family history of heart disease, have severe chest pain, unstable angina (which comes on at rest), or are awaiting procedures such as angioplasty, bypass surgery or heart transplant.

Supplementary Benefits

Ideally we should get all the nutrients we need from the food we eat. However there are times in all of our lives when we may need extra vitamins, minerals and trace elements. If you lead a busy, active life, drive a car through traffic, live or work in the city, have a stressful job, skip meals or eat irregularly, you may benefit from a daily multi-vitamin and mineral supplement to protect your body from disease and premature ageing. Ideally this should be individually prescribed for your needs with the help of a qualified naturopath or nutritionist.

POWER JUICES

Freshly made juices are a convenient, easy way to ensure that you get your daily quota of fruit and vegetables. Being high in water content they help flush toxins from the body and are restorative, cleansing and calming. Fresh juices are low in calories, high in nutrients and virtually fat-free, which makes them one of the healthiest and most effective ways to curb appetite if you are trying to lose weight.

TRY THE FOLLOWING:

- **Tomato: to cleanse the blood and liver, and to eliminate toxins.**
- **Orange and papaya: to improve digestion and cleanse the intestines.**
- **Green juices (*eg* broccoli, cabbage): to improve the condition of hair, skin and eyes.**
- **Raspberry and grape: detoxifying, astringent, keeps skin healthy and improves kidney function.**

Detoxification Matters

Just as important as eating well is periodic detoxification, designed to dissolve and clear out toxins and stored wastes from the lungs, kidneys, liver, skin and bowels. Detoxification also restores cellular balance, rests the system and encourages all the organs and tissues to function properly.

Throughout the ages fasting has been used by doctors and believers to cleanse and purify both body and mind. Regular detoxification can help you look younger, weigh less, slow ageing, improve flexibility in your joints, increase fertility and enhance the senses. And detoxification does not just clear the body; it also helps restore mental balance, leading to a more organised, more creative, motivated, relaxed, energetic, clear and conscious you.

The Spa Experience

The Spa Experience

Ancient beliefs of the East (above) work in harmony with advanced therapies. The serene environment of the Chiva-Som spa evokes positive well-being (right).

A healthy, enjoyable and successful life relies upon the careful maintenance of mind, body and spirit. If any one of these suffers an imbalance, the complete well-being of the individual is affected. In today's demanding society, regular imbalances to our day-to-day well-being are all too common, occurring at all age levels; as individuals, we try to address such symptoms as an unfit physique, weak nervous system or mental fatigue, while maintaining a constant pace in our professional and personal lives. A tough assignment, especially with people nowadays living substantially longer and needing to sustain optimum health and energy levels to fully enjoy their prolonged lives. This is where a good spa can provide the required holistic approach.

Spas of international standard offer a diverse choice of consultations, positive health treatments, exercise and fitness classes, indoor and outdoor activities, nutritional advice, diet and stress management programmes – all of which aim to enhance, restore and renew the individual and thus to develop a wider spectrum where mind, body and spirit work in unison.

Healing

The accent is always on the positive aspects of health – prevention rather than cure, innovation rather than accepted practice, the application of wisdom rather than the passive acceptance of ageing.

Professionals will have set the standards in medical and health advice and will have devised appropriate treatments. During their stay, guests of all ages and fitness levels will aim at optimising their personal aspirations: that is, to achieve some immediate, tangible benefits, to learn how to extend these into a lifestyle and to have fun.

In tracing the root of every health problem, or better still, in anticipating

Luxurious vegetation and traditional Thai landscaped gardens at Chiva-Som.

a health problem, positive well-being can be attained, as the symptom(s) can be better addressed through understanding and purpose. From an initial private consultation upon arrival with one of the medical staff, to the most up-to-date and effective therapies available, treatments are tailored to suit individual needs rather than fit general types.

Exercises in the pool, whether swimming or aqua-aerobics, challenge the body's muscles.

The Spa

While the individual may benefit from water therapies due to its mineral content, which rectifies the body's imbalances, water is also crucial for providing natural and comforting support, acting as a balance for the body's temperature, while natural effervescence functions through certain thermal waters. The spa dimension is not simply cosmetic – its aim is to give guests a safe base from which to address any stress or health problems they may have. It altogether complements the basic philosophy: to unite the healthy state of body, mind and spirit.

Symbolically, water is a natural cleanser, and while it washes impurities away it also replenishes the body of many deficiencies. Hydrotherapy, popularised by 19th century German physician Kneip, usually involves the application of water which is alternatively hot and cold, to improve the activity of the body's main systems. As a result, circulation is improved, muscle and tissue are toned and cellulite problems are checked. Other water facilities will include a pool for aqua-aerobics and swimming, a flotation tank, a hydro Jacuzzi, a Kneip therapy bath of pebbles in cold and hot pools to massage the feet and a steam room.

Other water sports, from sailing to windsurfing, may also be available at the spa or nearby.

The newest technologies can be applied to health and beauty treatments in the spa, developed in co-operation with leading international experts in the fields of holistic medicine and hydrotherapy. Separate heat treatment facilities will feature saunas, steam rooms, Jacuzzis, cool plunge pools and relaxation lounges. Treatment rooms will offer such therapies as aromatherapy, Thai or Swedish massage, in addition to specific face and body treatments – from body scrubs and wraps, to reflexology, electrical face and body reshaping and toning. The range of facial treatments should cater to all skin types; with the use of plant and flower extracts, fragile skin or delicate complexions are naturally hydrated, leaving them younger-looking and radiant.

Other facials go beyond skin-deep, by purifying and nourishing, with use of a gentle skin regime that comprises refining, lymph drainage, pressure point massage and specific active aromatherapy products. The complexion

DELUXE HYDROTHERAPY WITH ESSENTIAL OILS

– 30 minutes

With the use of essential oils and bath salts, the guest is submerged in a bath. Jets of water are gradually propelled, starting from the feet, working up to the legs, torso, arms and back; at each elevation the jets stop and only concentrate on the one area. The action is pummelling without discomfort, and the guest emerges feeling stimulated and calm. (This is just one of the hydrotherapy treatments available at the spa.)

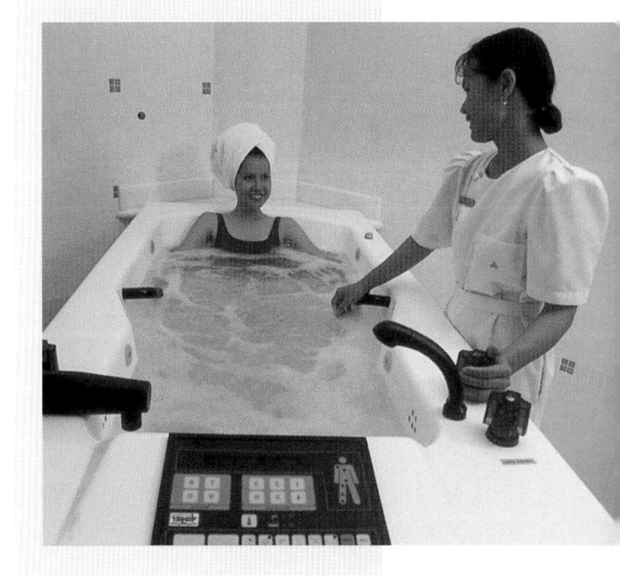

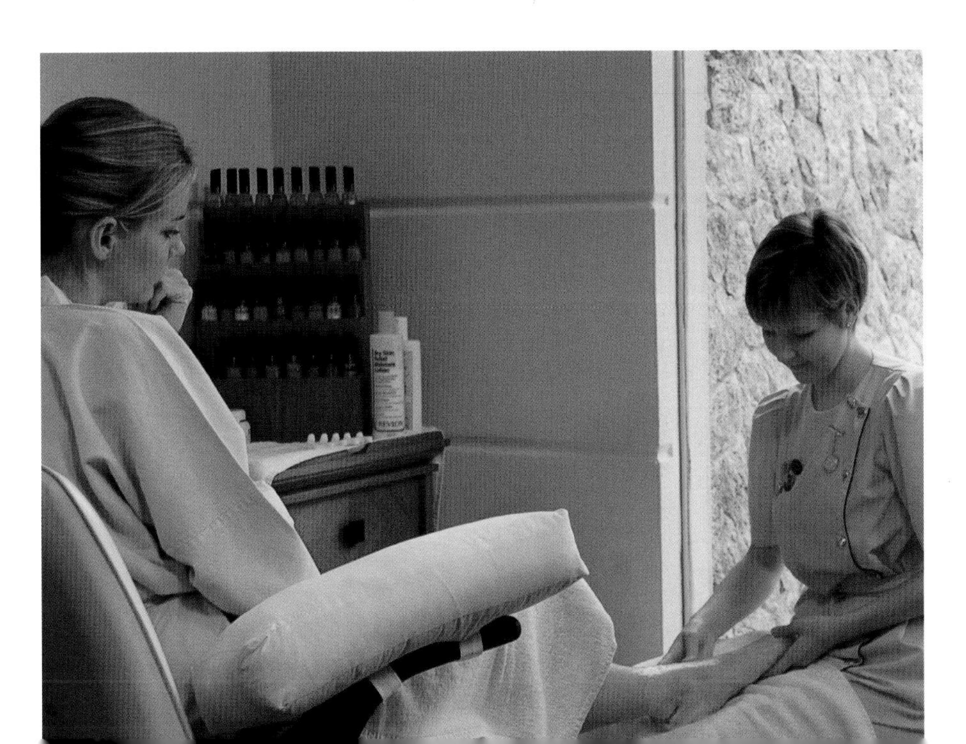

Qualified therapists specialising in a diverse range of beauty care offer helpful tips for guests to enhance their personal beauty regimes.

The Jacuzzi is an integral part of the spa's heat/water treatments. It stimulates and relaxes while increasing body and lymphatic circulation. Besides releasing built-up tension, massage improves the circulation of both blood and lymphatic fluid (below), which drains away toxic wastes. At Chiva-Som, there are dedicated outdoor massage pavilions.

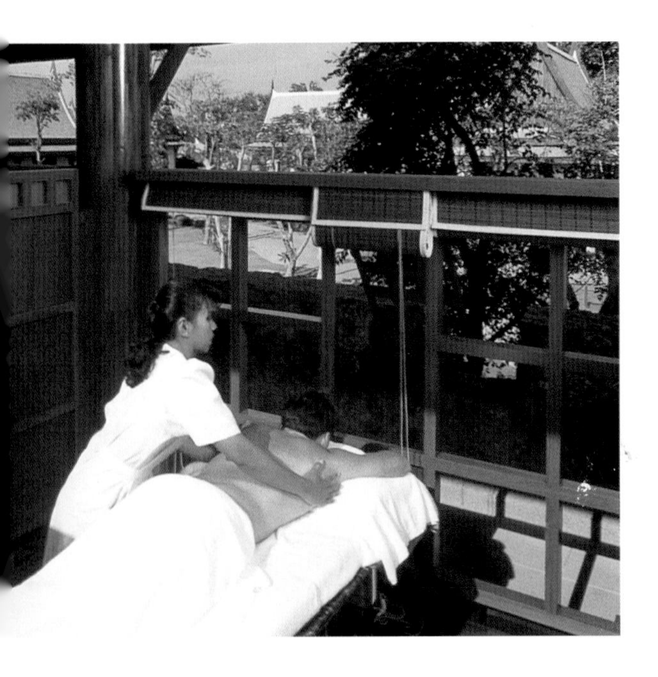

and skin condition reveal the essence of an individual's health; rashes and blemishes can be tell-tale signs of a hormone imbalance, stress, diet or an irregular skincare regime. Modern environments and harsh climates attack the skin's natural immunities, leaving it sensitised and irritated, as well as accelerating the skin's ageing process. A wise choice of natural ingredients, together with an effective diet can help soothe and calm any number of problem skins.

Medical Expertise

Although spas cater more for well rather than sick patients, their programmes can be effective and tailor-made for treating ailments such as muscular and skeletal disorders, skin problems, stress-related illnesses, cardiac rehabilitation and heavy smoking. For example, insomnia can be treated through meditation, and the methods should be equally good when practised by guests in their own home environment. Simple forms of meditation are demonstrated by the experienced staff, comprising gentle breathing and concentration of the mind, inducing a combined sense of calm and drowsiness which produces a sound state for mind and body to sleep.

The medical department will offer a special range of treatments aimed at improving the efficiency of the immune system, rejuvenation and anti-ageing. This includes equilibropathy to help maintain the flow of energy and keep the body in healthy balance; physiotherapy to correct skeletal, muscular and postural imbalances; iridology to diagnose deficiencies in the organs; allergy testing and various weight loss programmes under medical supervision. The Reiki technique, the Japanese 'universal life energy', a gentle method of applying pressure to specific areas of the hands to channel energy in a particular pattern over the body, is just one of them. It encourages the body's own healing ability, going to the core of the problem and creating a synthesis between mind, body and spirit.

An Exercise Programme to Fit

Exercise is a key part of a healthy lifestyle, and guests will be able to choose from a wide range of classes, from specialised Pilates sessions in air-conditioned studios with sprung floors to contemplative yoga, preferably outdoors. An invigorating morning power walk along the beach or a country

MARINE ALGAE BODY MASK – *60 minutes*

On her back on a pre-heated bed the guest's entire body is smothered in a rich warm mask solution. Upon turning over, the rest of the body is covered, and is then wrapped in a clingfilm-like plastic sheet, with a thermal blanket laid on top and towels to cover the neck and feet. The guest is

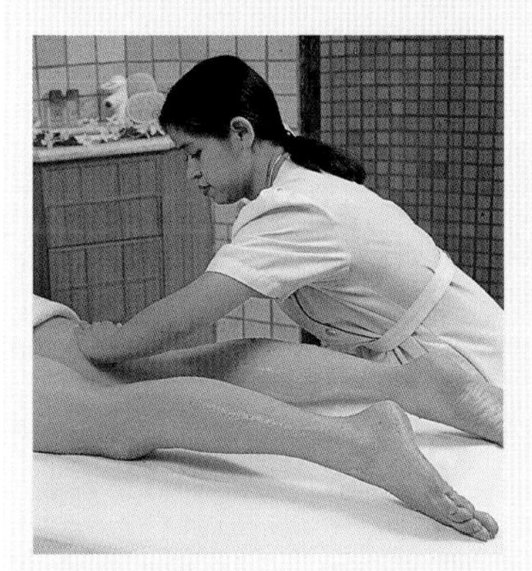

then left to relax for 10 minutes, after which the layers are gently removed. After a warm shower, to wash off the mask, the guest should lie back on the pre-heated bed, and the therapist wraps the body in foil and leaves the guest to relax for 15 minutes. After a further shower, the whole body is then moisturised.

A mountain-bike ride – one of the best outdoors workout.

HOLISTIC AROMATHERAPY TOTAL BODY CARE –
90 minutes

This treatment begins with pre-heat Jacuzzi and sauna for 10 minutes. The guest is then led to a room and asked to lie down on a therapy bed. The body is brushed with gentle strokes from a bristle brush from head to toe, each limb brushed separately, the back and shoulders, the chest and waist area. A more vigorous treatment from an exfoliating cleanser then follows, after which the guest is invited to shower and return to the bed. While the areas to be massaged are isolated, the rest of the body remains warm under the soft cotton towels. The room temperature is perfectly balanced and gradually the sensation of aromatic oils that are being absorbed into the skin sink in and the guest will naturally begin to feel drowsy. Time becomes immaterial and soon the therapist will work her way up the back and arms and

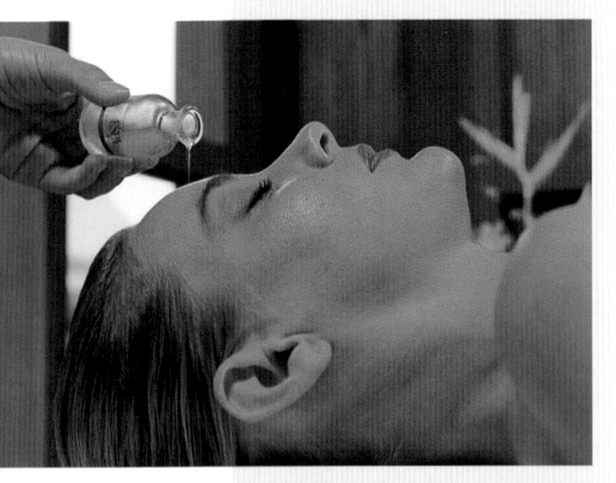

repeat the massage on the other side. The guest should feel in equilibrium with their own body as the therapists' expert long, soft strokes relax all the tense muscles. After a while the attention is switched to the face, which is cleansed and moisturised. Then, the scalp receives a revitalising massage.

lane can prompt the best start to the day, while a mountain-bike ride at a gentle pace in the late afternoon offers the perfect opportunity to work out while enjoying the most scenic views. Supervisory help in all sports will be provided, with personal fitness programmes adapted to individuals with special requirements.

One advanced facility available in the best gyms is oxygen-power fitness, comprising a controlled exercise programme of four to ten sessions enhanced by a combination of vitamins and minerals and the inhalation of oxygen under medical supervision (see page 14 for more details). The programme is designed for men and women of all ages, ranging in status from untrained to professional athletes, to help improve endurance, stamina, and general *joie de vivre*. Measurement of oxygen levels and a full medical check-up are performed prior to the commencement of the programme.

Nutrition

No attempt to improve oneself is complete without proper attention to diet and nutrition. The vast and varied array of dishes featured in the next section (see from page 58 onwards) is a proof that healthy eating need not be equated to uninspiring food. Meals need to be both nutritionally balanced and regularly scheduled through the day, ensuring an adequate daily intake of food without experiencing cravings between meals.

As many organically grown ingredients as possible should be used, to avoid the absorption of pesticides. The recipes will make the best use of therapeutic foods such as ginger and lemon grass, which provide essential nutrients and minerals.

In addition to offering the freshest and most wholesome of menus on its premises, the spa may also offer its own food line, from natural fruit spreads and low-calorie cookies to no-oil salad dressings and salt substitute.

A Little Less is Easy

If the guest's intention is to lose weight during their stay, a dietician can advise a realistic and effective programme to help them attain the desired target weight. A nutritional analysis will offer advice to those wishing to improve their eating habits. The reduction of salt is an integral part of a healthy diet. The use of high sodium foods such as soya sauce or nam pla (Thai fish sauce)

Healthy eating does not need to be boring – it just requires a sensible combination of tasteful natural ingredients.

will add more than a sufficient complexity of flavours without salt. Additional salt substitute seasonings such as fresh herbs and spices (particularly garlic, ginger, blend peppers, tarragon, coriander, chilli and any of the lemon-scented herbs) are used in abundance. Likewise, cooking methods such as steaming, poaching and baking are healthier alternatives to frying. Fruit purées, pumpkin, sweet potato, vegetable stock and apple concentrate are excellent fat substitutes when used in the correct context. Examples appear throughout the Recipe section of this book, from page 58 onwards.

Lentil salad (left) is just one of the mouth-watering, nutritious dishes prepared at Chiva-Som, the full recipe of which is featured in the Recipe section (see page 88).

FLOTATION – ***30 minutes***

After a brief shower the guest is led into a chamber comprising a conical-shaped ceiling and a circular pool. No extenuating fixtures are apparent. Stepping into the pool to float on their back, the guest will observe that the pool is only 2-3 feet in depth. At first it is a strange sensation, as the water temperature matches the body's temperature and there is gradually a feeling of weightlessness – the principle

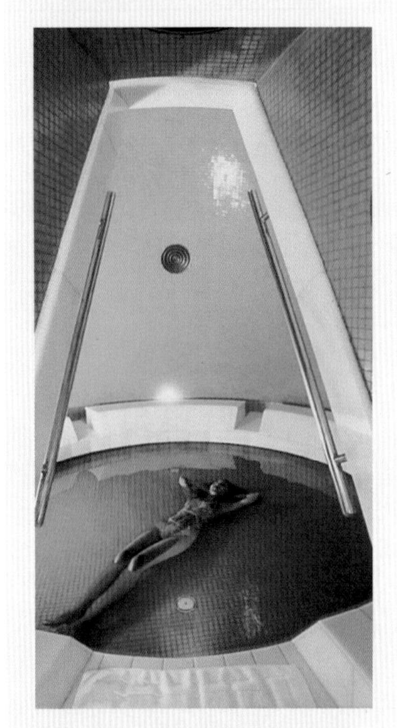

behind flotation is for the body to completely let go and relax. Then the guest slips into neutral mode, where both body and mind voluntarily become inactive. After 30 minutes the therapist gently summons the guest awake. It is advised that guests do not exert themselves directly after the treatment, as there is a tendency towards drowsiness.
Flotation reduces heart rate, oxygen consumption and levels of stress chemicals in the bloodstream.

Great emphasis is given to the intake of liquids, as this helps specific functions of the body, including digestion and lymphatics. Guests are encouraged to drink ample quantities of mineral water, both at mealtimes and in-between, to keep the requisite intake levels topped up.

Chiva-Som: Putting the Theory into Practice

Conceptualised by Mr Boonchu Rojanastien, Thailand's former Deputy Prime Minister, the exclusive spa resort was created by international consultants in the field of health and leisure from England and France.

On an exclusive beachfront setting in Thailand's royal resort of Hua Hin on the Gulf of Siam, Chiva-Som's seven acres have been planned to exude a relaxing environment for all its guests. At the heart of the resort is the ultra-modern spa with its impressive array of facilities. From exfoliation treatment to Swedish massage, flotation to iridology, Chiva-Som has combined modern equipment with the latest in medical research to offer comprehensive programmes where the guest is invited to consider healthier alternatives to all aspects of his lifestyle, leading to permanent changes. At Chiva-Som, exercise is a key feature in optimising personal health goals; from aqua-aerobics in the bathing pavilion, to power walking along the beach or a round of golf, the resort caters for all levels of physical activity.

Sunrise over the Gulf of Siam and the Chiva-Som resort.

The concept behind the design of the Chiva-Som resort is to provide an environment conducive to the adoption of long lasting health habits.

Chiva-Som's culinary expertise is evident in the varied and wholesome dishes offered daily, all of which are carefully balanced in flavour and nutritional value, and are prepared using the freshest ingredients harvested from the resort's own organic garden.

Chiva-Som aims to educate as well, and lectures in different fields are scheduled on a regular basis. These can range from talks on holistic healing and stress reduction to beauty or the culinary arts. While guests arrive at Chiva-Som with varying goals, frequently they leave with more than they anticipated – whether the intention is to become healthier and fitter, toned, pampered and beautified or to overcome a particular health problem or stress-induced ailment, Chiva-Som provides the elements for a commitment to long-lasting health habits.

The Recipes

Beauty Express

85 Calories • 0.6g Fat • Serves 4

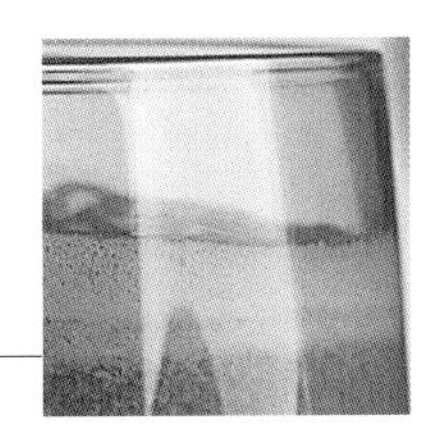

100g raw spinach
• ***4 carrots***
• ***2 green apples***
• ***600ml water***

1 Wash the vegetables thoroughly. Do not peel the apples or carrots. Remove seeds from the apples. **2** Cut into pieces that will fit into the shute of a vegetable juicer. **3** Pass the apple pieces, spinach, and carrot through the juicer. Add water to thin the juice to the desired consistency and serve.

Banana Oatmeal Shake

310 Calories • 5.6g Fat • Serves 4

800ml low-fat milk
• ***4 bananas***
• ***12 dates***
• ***2 tbsps oat bran***

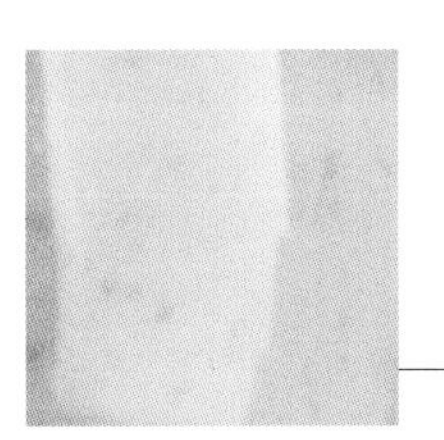

1 Peel the bananas. Remove seeds from the dates. **2** Place the bananas, dates, low-fat milk and oat bran in a food blender and blend together until smooth. Pour into a glass and serve.

Kiwi Crush

140 Calories • 0.8g Fat • Serves 4

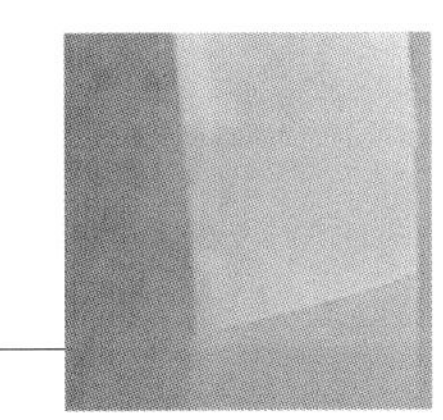

4 kiwi fruits
• ***2 green apples***
• ***250g green grapes***
• ***600ml cold water***

1 Wash the grapes and apples. Remove seeds from the apples. It is not necessary to remove the stems from the grapes, or the apple peel. **2** Peel the kiwi fruits. Pass the prepared fruit through a vegetable juicer. **3** Add the cold water to the juice, mix well and serve.

Nutritional note: All calorie and fat calculations given with each recipe refer to a single serving, unless otherwise indicated in the recipe itself.

Chiva-Som Muesli

220 Calories • 4.0g Fat • Serves 4

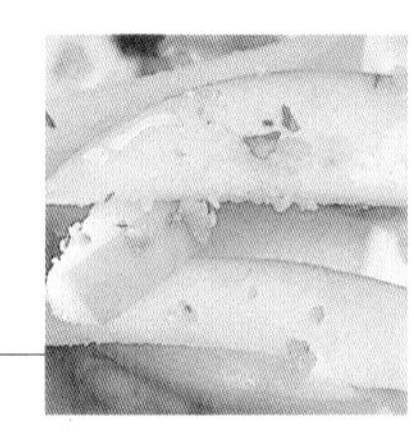

1 litre low-fat yoghurt • 4 tbsps oatmeal • 4 tbsps raisins
• 1 tsp walnuts, roasted and chopped
• 1 tsp almonds, roasted and chopped
• 1 tbsp honey • 2 green apples

1 Wash the apples thoroughly, and leaving the skin on, cut into fine strips of equal length. **2** Place in a bowl with the oatmeal, raisins, honey and nuts. **3** Fold the yoghurt into the muesli mixture and set aside for 5 minutes for the oatmeal to soften. Serve.

Apple and Prune Compote

185 Calories • 0.5g Fat • Serves 4

4 apples
• 20 prunes, pitted
• 125ml water

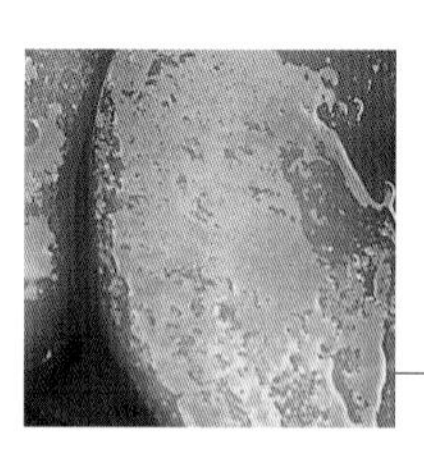

1 Wash the apples thoroughly. Cut each apple in half, removing the seeds. Leaving the skin on, cut the apple halves into thin wedges. **2** Place the wedges in a saucepan with the prunes and water. Cover with a close-fitting lid, and place over a medium heat. Bring to the boil, and simmer for 3 minutes. **3** Remove the lid and gently stir the fruits. Replace the lid and continue to cook the fruits until they are just softened. The compote can be served either hot or cold.

Blueberry Pancakes

150 Calories • 1.4g Fat • Serves 4

65g flour • 3 tbsps baking-powder • 2 tbsps sugar
65ml skimmed milk • 125ml soda water • 1 egg white
225g blueberries • 2 egg whites • 1 tsp oil (or non-stick cooking spray)

1 In a mixing bowl, combine the flour, baking-powder, sugar, milk, soda water and one egg white. Beat well until combined. Fold in the blueberries. **2** Beat the two remaining egg whites until stiff and fold into the bowl. **3** Lightly brush a non-stick frying-pan with oil and warm over a medium heat. Pour in a quarter of the mixture, tilting the pan to spread it evenly. **4** Return to the heat and cook until the edges start to brown and curl slightly. Carefully flip the pancake, to cook the other side. Turn out, and roll slightly. Serve with blueberry coulis (see page 119).

Mushroom and Tomato Omelette

105 Calories • 3.1g Fat • Serves 4

8 egg whites • 8 tbsps low-fat milk • 1 tsp oil • 125ml vegetable stock • 4 tomatoes, peeled and deseeded • 1 small onion, finely chopped • 80g mushrooms, chopped

1 In a non-stick frying-pan place the chopped onion and half the vegetable stock. Simmer until the onion becomes soft, adding extra stock if necessary. **2** Add the mushrooms and cook until the stock has almost evaporated. **3** Dice the tomatoes and add to the pan to cook for one minute. Set the mixture aside. **4** Wipe out the pan with a dry cloth, and using a brush, lightly oil the sides. Place on a high heat. **5** Meanwhile, beat the egg whites and milk together until they are well combined, but not too frothy. Pour into the hot pan and cook until almost set. **6** Pile the filling into the centre of the omelette, and gently fold over. Turn the pancake out onto a plate and serve immediately.

Tip: Because egg yolks are not used, the omelette will not 'roll' with the same elasticity as a regular full-fat omelette.

Khao Tom
Thai-Style Rice Soup

There are three variations for this recipe, to suit all preferences.

130 Calories / 1.4g Fat (mushrooms) • 155 Calories / 1.4g Fat (fish) • 160 Calories / 2.1g Fat (chicken) • Serves 4

1.2 litres vegetable stock • 50g cooked long-grain rice • 35g cooked wild rice • 70g cooked brown rice • 150g mushrooms, sliced (for Khao Tom Het) or • 200g chicken, minced (for Khao Tom Gai) or • 200g fresh fish, sliced (for Khao Tom Pla) • black pepper • 4 tbsps nam pla (or light soya sauce) • fresh ginger, chopped • 1 spring onion, chopped • crushed dried chilli • coriander leaves

1 Pour the stock into a saucepan and bring to the boil. Add the cooked rice and simmer for 5-6 minutes, or until the rice starts to break up. **2** For 'Khao Tom Het', add sliced mushrooms and bring back to the boil. For 'Khao Tom Gai' roll the minced chicken into balls and cook in the rice for 5 minutes. For 'Khao Tom Pla', add the sliced fish and cook in the rice for 2-3 minutes. **3** Season with pepper and nam pla. If the soup becomes too dry, add a little more stock. **4** Add ginger, spring onion, chilli and coriander leaves to taste, or serve each of these separately in small dishes as accompaniments.

Orange and Oatmeal Muffins

125 Calories per muffin • 0.8g Fat • Makes 12

MUFFINS: ***200g instant oatmeal • 250ml orange juice • 200g wholemeal flour • 100g sugar • 1 tsp baking powder • 1 tsp baking soda • 2 egg whites, lightly beaten***

TOPPING: ***3 tbsps instant oatmeal • 1 tbsp orange juice • 1 tsp sugar***

1 Mix the oatmeal and orange juice together, then set aside to soak for 20 minutes. Meanwhile, combine topping ingredients. **2** Mix flour with baking powder and soda. Add the sugar and lightly beaten egg whites. **3** Stir the beaten eggs and sugar into the oatmeal mix, and spoon into non-stick muffin tins. Sprinkle a little of the topping mix over each muffin. **4** Bake at 160°C/310°F/Gas Mark 2 for 12-15 minutes or until the muffins are springy but firm to the touch.

Cranberry Muffins

105 Calories per muffin • 0.9g Fat • Makes 12

200g instant oatmeal • 125ml skimmed milk • 200g wholemeal flour • 1 tbsp baking powder • 100g cranberries • 2 egg whites • 65ml apple concentrate

METHOD 1: **1** Combine the apple concentrate and cranberries in a saucepan. Cover and place over a low heat, and bring to the boil slowly, continuing to cook until some of the berries burst. Remove from the heat and set aside to cool. **2** Combine all remaining ingredients together, then add the cooked berry mix. **3** Pour into non-stick muffin tins and bake at 165°C/320°F/Gas Mark 2 for 15-18 minutes. Remove from the oven and cool on a wire tray. METHOD 2: Combine all ingredients together, pour the beaten mixture into non-stick muffin tins and bake at 165°C/320°F/Gas Mark 2 for 15-18 minutes. Cool on a wire tray.

Purée of Eggplant with Lime

75 Calories • 5.7g Fat • Serves 4

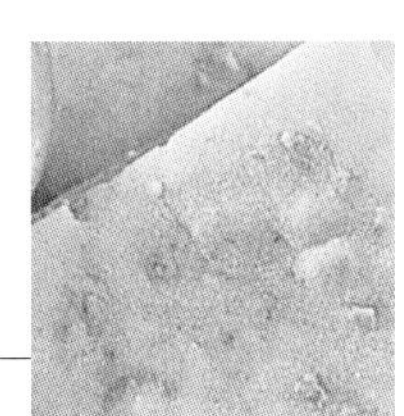

300g eggplant or aubergine
• 2 cloves garlic • 2 tbsps sesame seeds
• juice of 2 limes
• black pepper • 1 tbsp olive oil

1 Cut eggplants in half and place on a baking tray with the cut surfaces facing upwards. Bake until soft. Cool. **2** In a food processor, blend the sesame seeds to a paste. Add lime juice and garlic. **3** Scoop out the flesh of the eggplants and add to the food processor. Blend all together until smooth. (If too thick, add a little water.) Season to taste. Serve garnished with extra lime, a drizzle of olive oil and freshly ground black pepper. Traditionally served with pita bread.

Asparagus and Leek Terrine

85 Calories • 0.5g Fat • Serves 4

150g asparagus • 2 leeks • 6 gelatine leaves
• 250ml vegetable stock • 135g raspberries
• 6 tbsps herb salad dressing (see page 137)
• 6 lettuce leaves

1 Place a terrine mould in the refrigerator. **2** Peel and trim asparagus, removing woody base from each spear. Trim and wash the leeks, removing all dirt. **3** Boil a large pot of water and blanch the vegetables separately. **4** Refresh the vegetables in iced water, drain and pat dry with paper towel. **5** Warm the vegetable stock and dissolve the gelatine in it and season. Pour the liquid into the chilled terrine mould, wait one minute then pour back into a bowl. This is to line the mould with aspic. **6** Dip each asparagus spear in the aspic, and then begin layering them evenly in the terrine. Once one layer of asparagus is complete, then place a layer of leek. Continue layering the vegetables alternately until the terrine is full. **7** Pour over any remaining aspic and place the terrine in the refrigerator to set completely. **8** To make the dressing, take half the raspberries and place in a food blender with the herb salad dressing. Blend until smooth. Strain if desired, and adjust seasoning. **9** To serve, plunge the terrine quickly into hot water, then invert onto a board or tray. Using a warm sharp knife, carefully slice the terrine. Place a slice in the centre of each serving plate. Spoon the dressing around and garnish with remaining raspberries.

Ceviche of Sea Bass

115 Calories • 2.3g Fat • Serves 4

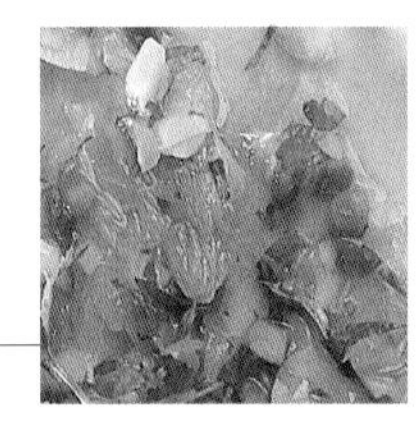

225g fresh sea bass fillets • a pinch of salt

• 1 clove garlic • 1 green bird chilli • 2 limes • 5g fresh coriander

SALSA: ***4 limes • ½ onion • ¼ tsp olive oil • 1 tomato***

• 15g coriander leaves, torn • pepper

1 Make the salsa first. Carefully remove the rind from the limes, and cutting between the membranes, remove the lime segments. Discard any seeds. Dice the flesh and place in a bowl. Finely dice the onion and add to the lime. Skin and deseed the tomato, and finely dice. Add to lime mix with the oil, chopped coriander and season with black pepper. Set aside for 2-3 hours. **2** Meanwhile, crush the garlic and rub this onto the base of a flat dish. **3** Thinly slice the fish across the grain and place on top of the garlic. Pour the juice and zest of 2 limes over the fish. Add chopped chilli, seasoning and chopped coriander. **4** Cover and refrigerate to absorb the flavours for 2-3 hours, or overnight. Spoon the salsa onto the centre of each plate and arrange the marinated fish around. Serve.

Tartare of Fish

170 Calories • 3.5g Fat • Serves 4

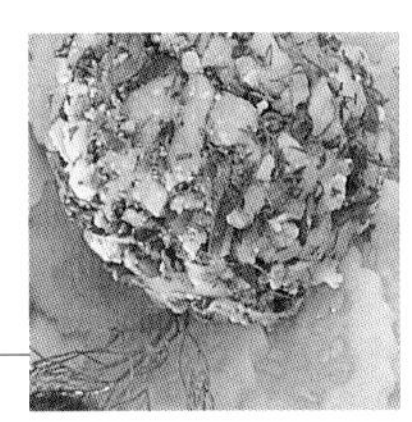

400g white fish fillets • 65ml lime juice • 2 spring onions, chopped • 1 tbsp parsley, chopped • 50g tofu • 1 cucumber • 1 tbsp dill • 2 tomatoes, diced • seasoning

1 Finely dice the fish fillets and tofu. Mix these with the lime juice, spring onions and parsley and set aside for 5 minutes. **2** Meanwhile deseed and dice the tomatoes finely and set these aside. **3** Peel and thinly slice the cucumber, then arrange the slices decoratively in the centre of each plate. **4** Season the fish mixture and drain off any excess liquid. Spoon onto the middle of the plated cucumber. **5** Decorate with the diced tomatoes and extra chopped dill. Serve well chilled.

Salmon Roulade

140 Calories • 5.6g Fat • Serves 4

100g fresh salmon • 100g smoked salmon • 50g low-fat ricotta cheese • 200g spinach, cooked • 1 tsp fresh dill • 50ml low-fat yoghurt • 1 lemon • 4 sprigs of dill • 1/2 tsp salt substitute (see page 140) • 1/4 tsp pepper • 4 lettuce leaves

1 Squeeze the cooked spinach to remove all excess water. In a food processor blend the ricotta, spinach and fresh salmon together until smooth. **2** Meanwhile lay out a piece of clingfilm. Over the clingfilm lay out the thin slices of smoked salmon to form a square. Spread the spinach mix over and season with a little pepper. **3** Carefully roll up the clingfilm to form a tight sausage and twist both ends to secure. **4** Place in a steamer and cook for 10 minutes. Remove and cool. **5** To make the sauce, combine chopped dill and salt substitute with the yoghurt. **6** To serve, remove the roulade from the clingfilm and cut it into slices. Spread a spoonful of the sauce on each plate and arrange a few roulade slices on top. Garnish with a lettuce leaf, lime slices and fresh dill.

Spinach and Mushroom Strudel

130 Calories • 1.2g Fat • Serves 4

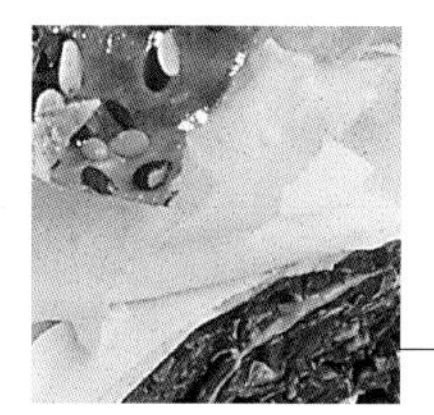

400g spinach, cooked • a pinch of nutmeg • 1 onion • 4 sheets filo pastry • 1 tsp sesame seeds • 200g mushrooms • black pepper • 2 tbsps low-fat yoghurt

1 Finely chop the onion and place in a saucepan with 60ml water. Cook until the onion has softened, adding extra water if it becomes dry. **2** Add sliced mushrooms and cook until dry. Add cooked spinach to the saucepan and season with nutmeg and pepper. Set aside in a colander to drain. **3** Meanwhile, lay out a sheet of filo pastry and brush edges very lightly with the yoghurt. Place a second sheet on top and repeat the process until it is all used. Do not brush the top sheet. **4** Take the drained spinach and mushroom mix and spread this evenly over the pastry, leaving a 2cm gap at the sides. Fold the sides in, then starting at the short end, roll up carefully but firmly. **5** Place on a non-stick baking sheet with the seam facing the bottom. Brush the top with any remaining yoghurt and sprinkle with sesame seeds. **6** Bake in a moderate oven, 180°C/350°F/Gas Mark 4 for 10-12 minutes or until golden in colour. Slice and serve.

Thai-Style Baked Filo Parcels

75 Calories • 0.7g Fat • Serves 4

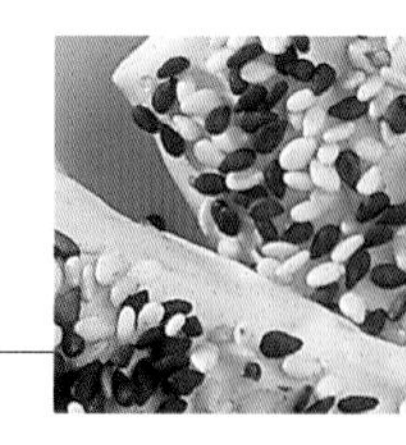

70g cabbage • 1 bell pepper • 150g mushrooms • 30g bean sprouts • 1/2 tsp fresh ginger • 1 tbsp fresh Thai basil • 1 small red chilli • 2 tbsps lime juice • 2 spring onions • 2 sheets filo pastry • 2 tbsps low-fat yoghurt • 1 tsp sesame seeds (optional)

1 Finely shred the cabbage, bell pepper and mushrooms. **2** Grate the ginger, chop the basil and chilli, and add to the raw vegetables. Finely chop the spring onions and add the lime juice. Mix all together and leave to stand for 30 minutes. Drain. **3** Cut each sheet of filo pastry into 4 pieces across the long side. Place a spoonful of the mixture onto the end of each strip of filo pastry and fold these strips into 'spring rolls'. **4** Place on a non-stick baking tray, and brush the tops very lightly with yoghurt. Sprinkle with sesame seeds. Bake at 200°C/400°F/Gas Mark 6 for 8-10 minutes or until the rolls have turned a golden colour.

Sashimi

160 Calories • 2.8g Fat • Serves 4

400g fresh fish fillets • 1 carrot, peeled and finely shredded • 1 small Japanese turnip, peeled and finely shredded • 4 tbsps soya sauce • 2 tsps wasabi

1 Choose very fresh fillets and chill well. **2** Place shredded carrot and turnip in a bowl of iced water to crispen up. **3** Trim and slice the fish fillets into medallions approximately 3cm x 3cm by ½cm thick. **4** To serve, drain the shredded vegetables and arrange on a platter. Arrange the fish decoratively on the platter. Serve the soya sauce and wasabi as side dishes. Serve immediately.

Mackerel 'Rollmops'

200 Calories • 3.2g Fat • Serves 4

400g fresh mackerel fillets • ½ tsp salt • 2 bay leaves • ½ tsp cloves, ground • 1 tsp mustard • 1 tsp pepper • 650ml vinegar • 1 onion • 1 cucumber • 6 slices wholewheat bread

1 Bring the vinegar to the boil with salt, bay leaves, ground cloves, mustard seed, peppercorns. Cool. **2** Shred the onion and cut cucumber into batons, removing the seeds. **3** Slice the mackerel into pieces approximately 5cm x 3cm. Take a piece of cucumber and a little onion, roll a piece of the fish around these and secure with a toothpick. Pack into a small jar. **4** Continue this process until all the fish is used. Layer any remaining onion on top, and pour over the vinegar. The vinegar should completely cover the fish. Seal and store in the refrigerator for 5-7 days before using. Serve with a small salad of apple and low-fat yoghurt, lettuce leaves and wholewheat bread.

Salmon and Vegetable Terrine

125 Calories • 6.8g Fat • Serves 12

600g fresh salmon fillets • 600ml fish stock • 2 tbsps herb vinegar • juice of 1 lime • 200g broccoli • 350g spinach • 225g carrots • 60g tomatoes • 6 gelatine leaves • chives • dill • seasoning

1 Slice the salmon fillets into escalopes and lightly poach them in the stock with the vinegar and lime juice for one minute. Drain and reserve the stock. **2** Blanch the spinach and broccoli separately in boiling water. Cut the carrots into long batons and blanch. Peel and deseed the tomatoes, dicing the flesh. **3** Dissolve the gelatine in the stock, and add the fresh herbs to make the aspic. **4** Line a terrine mould with clingfilm, then layer the terrine as follows: salmon, carrots, salmon, spinach, salmon, tomatoes, salmon and finally broccoli. **5** Add the aspic as you go. Cover and chill to set. **6** When completely set, turn out and carefully slice to serve.

Tom Yam Het
Hot and Sour Mushroom Soup

60 Calories • 1.1g Fat • Serves 4

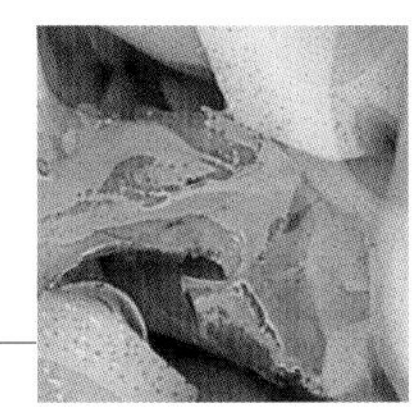

1 litre vegetable stock • 2 slices galangal or Thai ginger • 3 lime leaves • 3cm lemon grass • 150g cherry tomatoes • 1/2 tsp apple concentrate • 2 tbsps soya sauce • 2 tbsps lime juice • 2 fresh chillis (to taste) • 125g mushrooms (oyster or straw) • Thai basil • coriander leaves

1 In a large saucepan, bring the stock to the boil. Add galangal, lemon grass, lime leaves, soya sauce, apple concentrate and lime juice. Simmer for 2-3 minutes. Adjust the taste by adding the chillis, if preferred. **2** Bring the stock back to the boil and add the mushrooms and basil. **3** Stir well and garnish with fresh coriander before serving the soup hot.

Cucumber and Egg Soup

55 Calories • 0.9g Fat • Serves 4

2 small cucumbers, peeled and deseeded • 1 litre vegetable stock • 2 spring onions • 3 egg whites • 2 tbsps soya sauce • white pepper

1 Cut the cucumbers into thick slices. Place the slices in a saucepan with the stock and bring to the boil. **2** Add the onions and simmer for 4-5 minutes. Add the soya sauce and white pepper to taste. **3** Beat the egg whites and pour into the boiling soup, stirring continuously. Serve immediately.

Crab and Sweetcorn Soup

95 Calories • 1.2g Fat • Serves 4

170g crab meat • 1 tbsp Chinese wine • 1 tsp salt substitute (see page 140) • 1/2 tsp pepper • 1 tsp cornflour • 300g corn kernels • 1 litre vegetable stock • 2 egg whites • fresh coriander leaves, torn

1 Place the corn kernels in a blender, and pulse blend until coarsely chopped. **2** In a saucepan, bring the stock to the boil with the corn. Add seasonings, wine and crab meat. **3** Thicken the mixture slightly with the cornflour, and finally pour in the egg whites in a steady stream and beat. Remove the soup from the heat immediately and garnish with torn coriander leaves.

Chinese-Style Hot and Sour Soup

80 Calories • 1.9g Fat • Serves 4

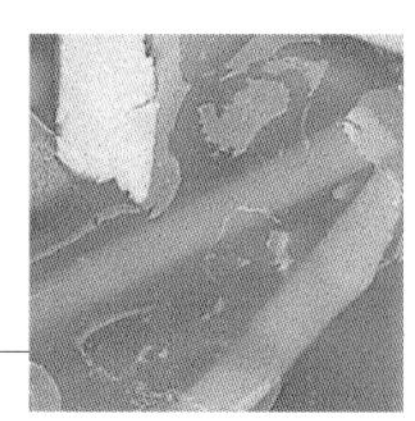

125g oyster mushrooms • 50g bamboo shoots • 50g cucumber • 1 tbsp ginger root • 100g tofu • 2 tsps soya sauce • 1 litre vegetable stock • 1 tbsp Chinese wine • pepper • red chilli to taste • 1 tbsp cornflour • 3 egg whites

1 Shred the mushrooms, bamboo shoots, cucumber (removing skin and seeds) and ginger root. Bring the stock to the boil and add the shredded vegetables. Simmer for 2-3 minutes. Add seasonings and chilli to taste. **2** Lightly beat the egg whites. Bring soup back to the boil, and while stirring continuously, add the egg whites in a steady stream. Thicken slightly with the cornflour. **3** Carefully shred the tofu and add to the soup. Heat through and serve.

Mexican Lime Soup

120 Calories • 3.0g Fat • Serves 4

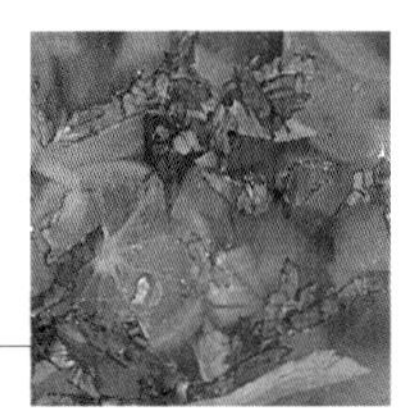

200g chicken breasts, skinless • 100g tomatoes, diced • 100g onions, diced • 3-4 chillis (to taste) • 3 tbsps fresh coriander, chopped • 1 litre vegetable stock • 125ml lime juice (to taste) • black pepper

1 Bring the vegetable stock to the boil, and gently poach the chicken breasts in the stock until they become tender. **2** Remove the chicken from the liquid, cool slightly and shred the meat. **3** Return the chicken to the stock, together with the diced tomatoes, onions, chillis and lime. **4** Bring the liquid to the boil and simmer for 2-3 minutes. Add the coriander and serve.

Chicken and Zucchini Soup

75 Calories • 1.8g Fat • Serves 4

100g chicken breasts, skinless and shredded • 300g zucchini or courgette sliced • 100g sliced mushrooms • 2 spring onions, chopped • 800ml vegetable stock • 1 tsp soya sauce • 1 tsp cornflour (optional) • black pepper

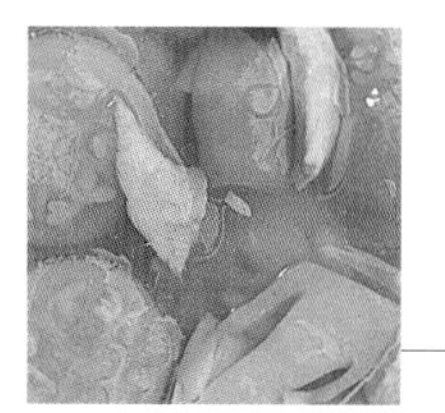

1 Bring the vegetable stock to the boil and add the shredded chicken, mushrooms, and the chopped spring onions. Season the stock with black pepper and soya sauce and simmer for 2-3 minutes. If preferred, thicken the soup slightly with cornflour. **2** Add the sliced zucchini. Cook until the zucchini is just tender, then remove from the heat and serve.

Glass Noodle Soup

70 Calories • 1.6g Fat • Serves 4

1 clove garlic, sliced • 750ml vegetable stock • 60g soft tofu, thickly sliced • 6 Chinese mushrooms, sliced • 135g glass noodles, soaked • 2 spring onions, sliced • 2 tbsps soya sauce • 1/2 tsp sugar • pepper • fresh coriander

1 Bring the stock to the boil. Add sliced garlic, sliced mushrooms, and noodles. Season to taste with soya sauce, sugar and pepper. **2** Add the thickly sliced tofu, and simmer until heated through. **3** Add the sliced spring onions. Serve garnished with torn coriander leaves.

White Bean Soup with Orange

100 Calories • 1.2g Fat • Serves 4

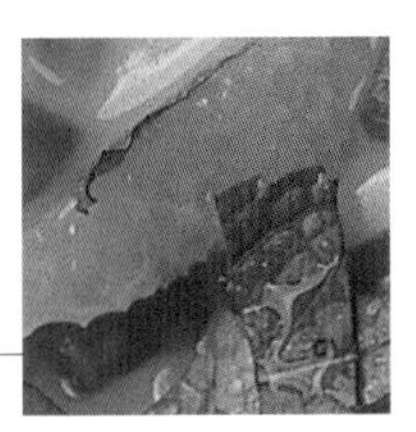

1 onion, chopped • 2 cloves garlic • 1.2 litres vegetable stock • 250g white beans, cooked • seasoning • 2 tomatoes, deseeded and diced • 1 orange, segmented • 1 tsp mint, chopped

1 In a large saucepan, place the chopped onions, garlic cloves and vegetable stock. Cover and bring to the boil. Simmer for 5 minutes. **2** Add the cooked beans and reboil. Remove from the heat, and cool slightly. Purée. **3** Return the purée to the saucepan and reheat. Adjust consistency with a little extra stock if necessary and season to taste. **4** Add the diced tomatoes, oranges and chopped mint. Fold all ingredients thoroughly together and serve.

Ginger Pumpkin Soup

75 Calories • 1.2g Fat • Serves 4

200g pumpkin, diced • 1 onion • 2 cloves garlic, crushed • 1/2 tsp ground coriander • 1/2 tsp allspice • 2 tbsps fresh ginger • 1.5 litres vegetable stock • pepper

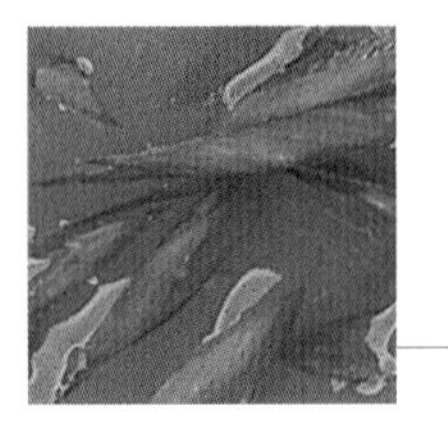

1 Peel and chop the pumpkin and onion. Place the prepared vegetables in a saucepan with the vegetable stock, garlic and spices. Bring to the boil, and then simmer until the pumpkin is cooked. **2** Purée to a smooth consistency and adjust seasoning to taste. Serve hot.

Banana Flower Salad

60 Calories • 2.3g Fat • Serves 4

250g banana flower, finely shredded • 2 tbsps shredded coconut, roasted • 2 tsps chopped almonds, roasted • 4 shallots, shredded • 2 spring onions • 3 chillis, chopped (to taste) • 2 tbsps nam pla (or light soya sauce) • 2 tbsps lime juice • 1 tsp honey

1 In a bowl, combine the coconut, almonds, shallots, spring onions – sliced, chillis, nam pla, lime juice and honey. **2** Add the banana flower to the bowl, and mix all the ingredients well. Serve the salad piled high on each plate.

Tip: If you would like to try this salad but do not have access to banana flowers, use cabbage instead. It has similar nutritional value.

Thai Seafood Salad

160 Calories • 2.8g Fat • Serves 4

400g mixed cooked seafood • 2 tomatoes • 1 Chinese celery • 1 onion • 2 spring onions • 15g coriander leaves • 2 tbsps lime juice • 1 tsp nam pla (or soya sauce) • 4 bird chillis (to taste, but should be spicy) • 1/2 tsp honey • 1 clove garlic • 2cm lemon grass • washed lettuce leaves

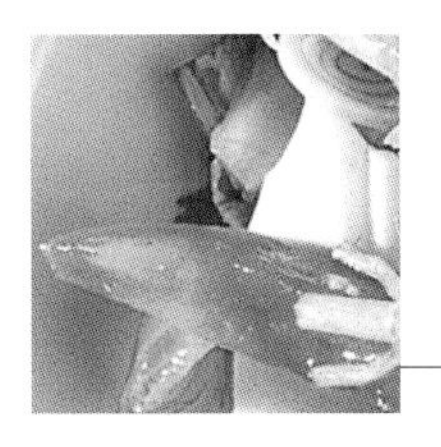

1 Crush the garlic and chillis together. Add the nam pla, lime juice and honey. Set aside. **2** Deseed the tomatoes and slice the flesh. Finely shred the lemon grass. Set aside. **3** Shred the celery, onion and spring onions and mix with the cooked seafood, together with the tomatoes, lemon grass, coriander and dressing. Serve on washed lettuce leaves.

Vietnamese-Style Chicken and Cabbage Salad

75 Calories • 1.0g Fat • Serves 4

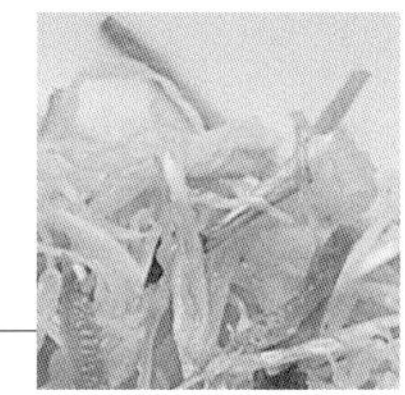

1 chilli • 1 clove garlic, crushed • 1 tsp apple concentrate • 1/2 tsp soya sauce • 3 tbsps lime juice • 1 tbsp water • 1/2 onion, finely shredded • 1 tbsp vinegar • 100g chicken breast, poached and finely shredded • 220g raw cabbage, finely shredded • 40g carrot, finely shredded • 1 tsp chopped parsley • 15g fresh coriander

1 Combine finely chopped chilli with the garlic, apple concentrate, soya sauce, lime, water, vinegar and onion. Leave to stand for 15 minutes, to help the flavours develop. **2** Add all the remaining ingredients to the dressing, mix thoroughly and serve.

Thai Eggplant Salad

80 Calories • 0.5g Fat • Serves 4

6 long green eggplant or aubergines • 2 spring onions • 4 shallots • 4 cloves garlic • 2 tbsps nam pla (or soya sauce) • 1 tsp apple concentrate • 2 tbsps lime juice • 2 tomatoes, seeded and diced • 15g fresh coriander leaves, torn

1 Bake eggplants on a tray in the oven until just soft. Cool and slice into rounds. **2** Shred the onions and shallots. Crush the garlic. **3** Toss all the ingredients together and serve.

Thai-Style Chicken Salad

150 Calories • 3.0g Fat • Serves 4

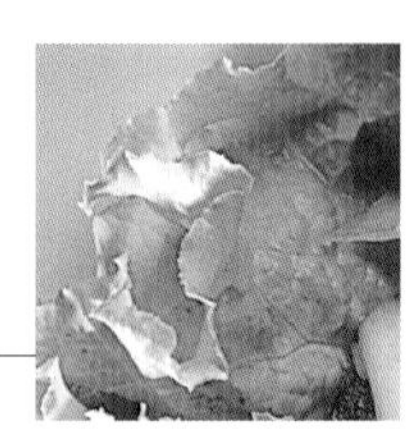

280g chicken breast, poached • 4 tomatoes • 1 Chinese celery • 1 onion • 2 spring onions • 15g coriander leaves • 2 tbsps lime juice • 1 tsp nam pla (or soya sauce) • 1/2 tsp honey • 1 clove garlic • 3-4 bird chillis

1 Crush the garlic and chillis together. Add the nam pla, lime juice and honey and combine well. **2** Deseed the tomato and slice the flesh. Set aside. Cut celery into 3cm lengths. Shred the onion. **3** Tear the cooked chicken into strips and mix with the celery, onion, tomato, parsley and dressing.

Green Papaya Salad

60 Calories • 1.0g Fat • Serves 4

½ green papaya • 2 cloves garlic • 2-3 chillis • 3 long beans, cut into 2cm lengths • 2 tbsps lime juice • ½ tsp apple concentrate • 1 tomato, deseeded and shredded • 1 tsp roasted almonds, chopped

1 Peel the papaya, discarding any seeds. In a food processor, or with a sharp knife, finely shred the papaya. **2** With a mortar and pestle, pound the garlic and chillis together. Add the long beans cut into lengths, and pound very lightly, just to bruise. Add the apple concentrate, papaya, lime juice and tomato. Mix all together. **3** Serve sprinkled with the chopped almonds.

Yam Yai
Mixed Vegetable Salad

80 Calories • 0.9g Fat • Serves 4

• 2 tbsps vegetable stock • 1 small onion • 2 small cucumbers • 1 stick celery • 2 long beans • 2 carrots • 3 spring onions • 2 tomatoes • 75g mushrooms • 2-3 chillis • 2 tbsps soya sauce • 2 tbsps lime juice • 1 tsp sugar • 1 clove garlic • 1 tsp roasted almonds, chopped • coriander leaves

1 Bring stock to the boil in a saucepan and add the chillis, soya sauce, lime juice and sugar. Stir and remove from the heat. **2** Add chopped garlic and nuts. **3** Cut the long beans into 2cm lengths. Shred the onion, celery and carrot. Slice the cucumbers, spring onions and mushrooms. Peel and deseed the tomato, cutting the flesh into thin strips. Mix the vegetables with the dressing and serve.

Long Bean Salad

80 Calories • 1.2g Fat • Serves 4

4 lettuce leaves • 400g long beans • 50g shallots, shredded • 3 medium tomatoes • 1 tbsp nam pla (or soya sauce) • 4 tbsps lime juice • 1/2 tsp honey • 2 tsps Thai basil • 4-6 bird chillis • 2 tsps roasted almonds, chopped • fresh coriander (optional)

1 Crush the garlic and chillis together. **2** Rub the beans slightly to break the surface and add to the garlic and chillis, together with the nam pla, lime juice, honey and spring onions. Mix well. **3** Roughly chop the tomatoes and basil, and add to the marinating beans, with the almonds. Mix gently. **4** Place on lettuce leaves and decorate with coriander (if used). Serve.

Lentil Salad

230 Calories • 1.6g Fat • Serves 4

600g green lentils (cooked) • 100g chicken breast, poached • 1 tomato • 1 green bell pepper • 3 spring onions • 2 tbsps balsamic vinegar • 1 tbsp apple concentrate • pepper

1 Dice the tomato and bell pepper. Shred the onion and chicken meat. **2** Combine with all remaining ingredients, and toss well to mix evenly. Season to taste and serve.

Japanese-Style Chilled Noodles

240 Calories • 4.2g Fat • Serves 4

4 shiitake mushrooms • 360g cooked prawn tails • 4 spring onions • 4 tsps fresh ginger • 4 tbsps soya sauce • 1 tsp sesame seeds • 180g somen noodles (fine white Japanese wheatflour noodles)

1 Soak the dried mushrooms in hot water for 10-15 minutes. Cool. When cold, slice. **2** Meanwhile, cook the noodles. Drain, and cool under cold running water. Refrigerate until required. **3** Prepare the garnishes by chopping the spring onion finely and grate the ginger. **4** To serve, place the chilled noodles in small serving bowls and top with the cooked prawns and sliced mushrooms. Sprinkle with sesame seeds. Serve onion, ginger and soya sauce in separate dishes as accompaniments.

Pan-Fried Snapper with Ginger and Mushroom Sauce

215 Calories • 2.7g Fat • Serves 4

4 x 150g snapper fillets • 1 tsp chopped coriander • 200g mushrooms • 2 tsps fresh ginger • 1 tsp Chinese wine • 1 tsp soya sauce • 1 tsp cornflour • 50ml vegetable stock • 4 small potatoes • mixed garden vegetables (beans, carrots, broccoli)

1 Wash and prepare the vegetables. Peel and boil the potatoes. When almost done, add the other vegetables and simmer. **2** Meanwhile place a little water with the fish in a non-stick frying-pan, skin-side down. Cook for 2-3 minutes. Remove and place on a warm plate. **3** Add the ginger, mushrooms and coriander to the pan and stir fry. Add the wine, soya sauce and vegetable stock. Thicken slightly with the cornflour and boil. **4** When the vegetables are cooked, drain and arrange them on each plate with the fish. Pour the sauce over the fish and serve.

Arabic-Style Baked Garoupa with Cumin

140 Calories • 3.7g Fat • Serves 4

600g garoupa fillets • 4 cloves garlic • 1/2 tsp cumin • 1/4 tsp turmeric • 1/4 tsp chilli powder • 20 ml lime juice • 5 ml olive oil • 1/2 tsp salt substitute (see page 140) • fresh coriander

1 Peel the garlic. Place in a spice grinder with the cumin, turmeric, chilli powder and salt substitute. Grind to a paste. **2** Add the oil and lime juice and mix well. **3** Rub the fish with the paste and set aside for 5-10 minutes. **4** Place in a baking dish and cook in moderate often for 10-15 minutes or until the fish is tender. Sprinkle with fresh coriander and serve.

Steamed Salmon with Basil and Shallots

260 Calories • 12.5g Fat • Serves 4

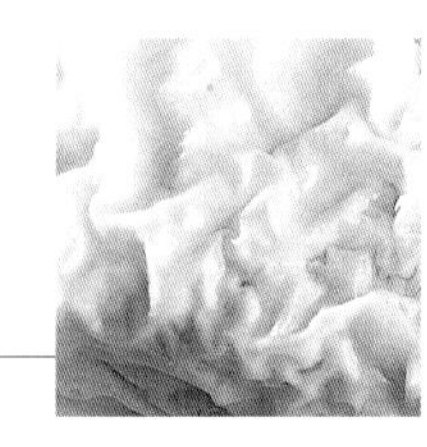

4 x 150g salmon steaks • 8 fresh Thai basil leaves
• 1 clove garlic • 3 shallots
• 1 tsp salt substitute (see page 140) • 4 sheets filo pastry
• 4 small cucumbers • 75ml vegetable stock

1 Peel and crush the garlic. Peel and chop the shallots. In a heavy-based saucepan, add the garlic and shallots together with 2 tablespoons of water. Cook to soften, adding a little extra water if it becomes too dry. Cool. **2** Lay out the salmon steaks and season with salt substitute, then top with the garlic mix. **3** Place two basil leaves on top, then wrap each steak in a sheet of filo pastry, ensuring the seam is on the bottom. **4** Place on a steaming plate or tray, and place in a steamer to cook. This will take 5-7 minutes. **5** Meanwhile, peel and deseed the cucumbers. Using a mandolin or sharp knife, cut the cucumbers into long spaghetti-like lengths. **6** Into a frying-pan, pour half of the stock and bring to the boil. Add the cucumber and toss to cook. Add a little more of the stock as it becomes absorbed. Do not overcook, as the cucumber will turn into mush. Season to taste. **7** To serve, arrange the strips on each plate and place the steamed salmon on top.

Tip: The filo pastry acts as a pasta dough, and will help to keep the fish hot and moist.

Ginger-Glazed Fillet of Sea Bass

250 Calories • 4.2g Fat • Serves 4

600g sea bass fillet • 1 tsp parsley • 200g mushrooms • 1 tsp ginger root, finely grated • 1 tsp sherry • 1 tsp soya sauce • 2 tsps cornflour • 4 carrots • 100g asparagus

1 Trim the asparagus and cut carrots into batons. **2** Combine ginger with sherry, soya sauce and cornflour. Set aside. **3** Place fish in a baking dish with the mushrooms and steam or bake in the oven for 5-7 minutes, or until done. **4** Meanwhile, steam the prepared vegetables. **5** Drain the juices from the cooked fish and add to the ginger mixture. Bring to the boil, (add a little vegetable stock or water if too thick) and spoon a little over the fish – this will keep the heat in the fish while you serve it. **6** Arrange the steamed vegetables on a plate with the fish. Spoon the remaining sauce over the fish and serve.

Snapper in Apple Juice

290 Calories • 4.4g Fat • Serves 4

4 x 150g snapper fillets • 1 green apple, peeled • 1 tsp lime juice • 125ml apple juice • 100g cooked pumpkin • 1 tbsp carrot, finely diced • 100g green beans • 4 small potatoes • 1 tsp parsley, chopped

1 Place the fish fillets in a small baking dish. Pour the apple juice and lime juice over the fish. Slice the apple very thinly and lay on top. **2** Bake in the oven for 8-10 minutes, or until the apple is cooked. **3** Meanwhile, blanch the carrot. Purée the pumpkin and then the blanched carrot. Reheat. **4** Steam the potatoes and beans until just tender. Roll the potatoes in the chopped parsley. **5** To serve, arrange the fish on a hot plate. Spoon a little of the reduced apple juice over, surround with the hot vegetables and garnish with fresh herbs.

Tuna with Grilled Vegetables

270 Calories • 3.8g Fat • Serves 4

4 x 150g tuna steaks • 1 large eggplant, diced and cooked • 12 small potatoes • 2 green peppers • 1 onion • 1/2 tsp marjoram • 1/4 tbsp olive oil • 1 zucchini

1 Place potatoes in a pan with water sufficient to just cover them. Cover with a lid and boil until soft. Remove from the water and cool. **2** Peel and thickly slice the onion. Wash and thickly slice the eggplant and zucchini. Cut the green peppers in half, removing the seeds, then into thirds. **3** Mix the marjoram with the oil and spread a little onto the tuna. **4** Toss all the vegetables together with the remaining marjoram and oil paste. Mix well and set aside for 5 minutes. To cook, cut the potatoes in half and place cut-side down under a hot grill. Add vegetables and then the fish. Turn the potatoes after 3-4 minutes to ensure they are heated through sufficiently, a total cooking time of 7-8 minutes. **5** Turn the vegetables and fish to cook each side, for the vegetables a total cooking time of 5-6 minutes, and for the fish, 4-5 minutes. Tuna is best served rare to medium. **6** Serve with lime slices and a sprig of fresh marjoram.

Norwegian Salmon with Mustard and Peppers

275 Calories • 13.1g Fat • Serves 4

600g salmon fillets (cut into 4 x 150g steaks) • 2 green peppers • 4 tbsps Dijon mustard • 1 egg white • 35g dried breadcrumbs • 125ml vegetable stock • 1 leek, white part only, cut into fine strips • 1 tbsp fresh dill, chopped • 2 carrots, cut into fine strips • white pepper

1 Skin the peppers, by holding over a flame until the skins turn black and blister. Place under running water, and wash off the burnt skins. **2** Cut each pepper open, remove and discard the stem and seeds. Finely dice the roasted flesh. Drain slightly and mix with the mustard and egg white. **3** Bring the stock to the boil, and then simmer until it has reduced by half. Season to taste with fresh dill and white pepper and put the finished sauce to one side. **4** Place the salmon, skin-side down, onto a non-stick baking sheet and spread with the prepared paste. Sprinkle with the breadcrumbs and place the baking sheet in a moderate oven, 180°C/350°F/Gas Mark 4 and bake for 10-12 minutes, or until cooked. **5** Remove from the oven and place under a hot grill to brown the breadcrumbs until golden. Meanwhile, steam the prepared leeks and carrots. **6** To serve, place the fish in the centre of each plate. Arrange the steamed vegetables around and spoon the dill sauce around the fish and over the vegetables.

Tip: While flaking indicates that fish is cooked, salmon is excellent when slightly undercooked.

Thai-Style Stir-Fried King Fish

300 Calories: • 2.0g Fat • Serves 4

600g King fish (or any other firm-flesh white fish) • 75ml fish stock
• 2 green chillis or 2 red chillis • 1 tbsp nam pla (or light soya sauce)
• 2 tsps fresh Thai basil (sweet basil is not suitable) • 2 cloves garlic • 1 onion
• 200g steamed rice (white, brown and wild rice grains combined)

1 Cut fish into medallions of approximately 1cm thick x 3cm diameter. **2** Crush the garlic. Peel and shred the onion. Shred the chillis, carefully removing the seeds. **3** Heat a wok or heavy frying-pan until hot, but not smoking. Add half the stock, shredded onion and crushed garlic and cook until dry, stirring continuously to prevent burning. **4** Add the remaining stock and fish medallions and stir fry for 3-4 minutes, taking care not to break up the fish. **5** Add chillis, basil, and nam pla. Mix well to coat the fish and serve with the mixed steamed rice.

Chinese-Style Steamed Sea Bass

150 Calories • 1.4g Fat • Serves 4

600g sea bass fillets • 3 dried Chinese mushrooms • 1 tsp fresh ginger • 3 spring onions • 2 tbsps soya sauce • 1 tsp salt substitute (see page 140) • 1 tbsp Chinese wine • ½ tsp apple concentrate • fresh coriander leaves

1 Soak the dried mushrooms in hot water for 10 minutes to soften. **2** Place fish on a plate and season with salt substitute. **3** Drain and slice the mushrooms. Shred the onions and cut the ginger into fine strips. **4** Mix these with the soya sauce, apple concentrate and wine. Pour over the fish. **5** Place in a steamer and cook for 4-5 minutes, or until just done. Do not overcook or the fish becomes dry. Serve sprinkled liberally with coriander leaves.

Baked Fillet of Sea Bass in Pastry

260 Calories • 2.1g Fat • Serves 4

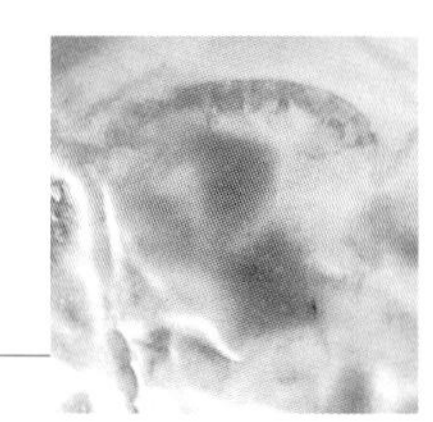

4 sheets filo pastry • 600g sea bass • 1 small carrot • 1 small leek • 4 sprigs dill • 1 red bell pepper • 1 stick celery • 4 slices lime • 4 slices garlic

SAUCE: ***1 small onion • 1 clove garlic • 2 carrots • 150 ml vegetable stock • fresh coriander***

1 Shred the carrot, leek, red pepper and celery and mix together. **2** Lay out the single filo pastry sheets and place a quarter of the vegetables onto each sheet. Top with slice of lime, garlic and dill sprig. Season with black pepper. Finish with 150g of sea bass. **3** Fold up the parcel and place on a non-stick baking tray. Ensure the fish is on top of the vegetables, and the seams are on the bottom. Brush with a little beaten egg white and bake at 180°C/350°F/Gas Mark 4 for 12-15 minutes, or until the parcels are golden in colour. **4** To make the sauce, chop the onion, garlic and carrots and place in a saucepan with the vegetable stock. Bring the vegetables to the boil and simmer until soft. **5** Purée the vegetables to produce a coulis and season to taste with fresh coriander. **6** To serve, place a spoonful of the carrot coulis in the middle of each plate and place one baked fish parcel on top. Garnish with extra sprigs of fresh dill.

Chicken with Black Bean Sauce

320 Calories • 4.8g Fat • Serves 4

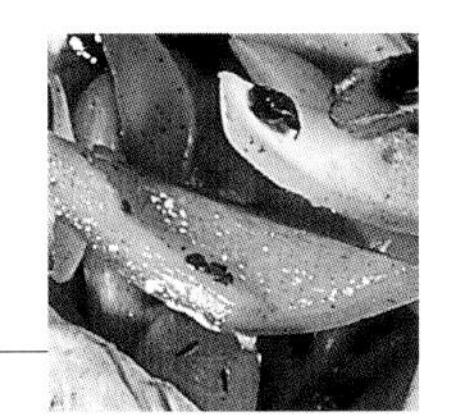

4 x 100g chicken breasts, skinless • 2 onions • 1 tsp fresh ginger, crushed • 1 clove garlic, crushed • 2 green bell peppers • 2 red bell peppers • 3 tbsps fermented black beans • 2 tbsps soya sauce • 125ml vegetable stock • 200g mixed steamed rice (brown, white and wild grains)

1 Cut the chicken into medallions and set aside. Peel and shred the onions. Cut the bell peppers in half, remove the seeds, then coarsely shred. **2** In a heavy-based frying-pan, add the garlic, ginger, onion and a little of the vegetable stock. Cook for 1-2 minutes. **3** Add the chicken pieces and stir-fry until they have coloured. Continue to add stock as the chicken absorbs the liquid. Add the bell peppers and continue to fry. **4** Add the beans and remaining stock, continue cooking for 1-2 minutes, or until the peppers are cooked but have retained their texture. **5** Season with fresh chilli and soya sauce. Serve the peppers with the mixed steamed rice.

Mongolian Beef

210 Calories • 6.7g Fat • Serves 4

400g beef fillet • 1 egg white • 2 tsps cornflour • 1 tsp salt substitute (see page 140) • 2 green peppers • 125ml vegetable stock • 1 tbsp fresh ginger, grated • 2 cloves garlic • 1 tbsp soya sauce • 2 tbsps Chinese wine • 2 carrots • pepper • ½ tsp apple concentrate • 2 chillis • 2 spring onions, cut into 2cm lengths

1 Slice the beef into thin slices. Place into a bowl. **2** Beat the egg white and add the cornflour and seasonings. Mix with the meat, and set aside for 1 hour. **3** Meanwhile, shred the carrots and dice the bell peppers. Finely chop the garlic and chillis, and mix with the ginger. **4** Heat a non-stick frying-pan and add 2 tbsps of the stock. Add the garlic mix, and cook for 1-2 minutes, adding a little extra stock if it becomes too dry. **5** Increase heat, and add the vegetables, then the beef, stirring continuously. Add extra stock as required. **6** Just before the meat is done, add the wine, soya sauce, apple concentrate and spring onions. Mix well and serve.

Bedouin Chicken

260 Calories • 5.0g Fat • Serves 4

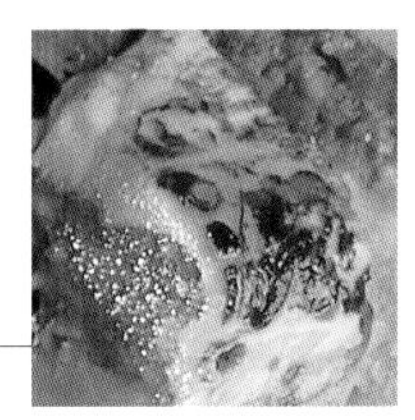

4 x 100g chicken breasts, skinless • 1 onion • 100ml vegetable stock • 1/2 apple, diced • 4 dates, chopped • 2 tbsps raisins • 1/4 tsp cinnamon • 1 tsp roasted almonds, chopped • 1/4 tsp allspice • 1/4 tsp pepper • 1/2 tsp salt substitute (see page 140) • pepper • 1 tbsp lime juice

1 Peel and finely chop the onion. Place in a saucepan with the vegetable stock and cook until soft and most of the stock has evaporated. Add raisins, dates, apple, almonds, cinnamon and allspice. Mix well then set aside. **2** Lay out the chicken breasts and carefully make an incision down one side to open out the breast. Season with salt substitute, pepper and lime juice. **3** Place the fruit mix in the centre of each breast and roll up each one tightly. **4** Wrap in aluminium foil, or secure with string and bake in the oven at 200°C/400°F/Gas Mark 6 until the chicken parcels are golden in colour. **5** Rest in a warm place for 5 minutes before slicing each parcel, to retain the juices in the meat. Serve with sautéed zucchini and bell peppers.

Breast of Chicken with Tomato Salsa

190 Calories • 4.2g Fat • Serves 4

4 x 100g chicken breasts • 125ml vegetable stock • 4 tomatoes • 2 tsps fresh coriander, chopped • 3 shallots • black pepper

1 Finely dice the shallots and combine with the coriander. **2** Peel and deseed the tomatoes. Squeeze out any juice from the skin and seeds into the onion mix, before discarding. Dice the tomatoes, and add to the onion mix. Season to taste with a little pepper. Set aside at room temperature for 30-60 minutes to allow flavours to develop. (The salsa will keep for up to 5 days in the refrigerator. Remember to bring the salsa to room temperature before serving.) **3** Heat the stock and gently poach the chicken breasts in the stock until they are almost cooked through. Care should be taken to avoid boiling the chicken, as this will toughen it. When the chicken breasts are almost cooked (4-5 minutes), switch off the heat and leave covered, for a further 5 minutes. **4** To serve, place each of the drained chicken breasts on a warm plate and spoon salsa around. An excellent accompaniment for this dish is a selection of steamed vegetables.

Chicken with Raisins and Pine Nuts

370 Calories • 8.3g Fat • Serves 4

4 x 100g chicken breasts • 40g raisins
• 40g pine nuts • 4 tbsps cider vinegar
• 200g brown rice, cooked
• 200g freshly steamed vegetables

1 In a food processor, blend raisins, pine nuts and vinegar to a paste. **2** Pour over chicken breasts, coating well and leave to stand for 1-2 hours. Place on a wire rack and grill, brushing with the marinade as the chicken cooks. Turn and grill on the other side, until the meat is cooked through, approximately 8-10 minutes. **3** Alternatively, bake in a moderate oven, or place in a non-stick frying-pan and pan fry. The oils in the pine nuts mean that no extra oil is required in the cooking. Serve with steamed vegetables and brown rice, heated through.

Nuea Paad Prig
Thai Veal with Chilli

170 Calories • 4.7g Fat • Serves 4

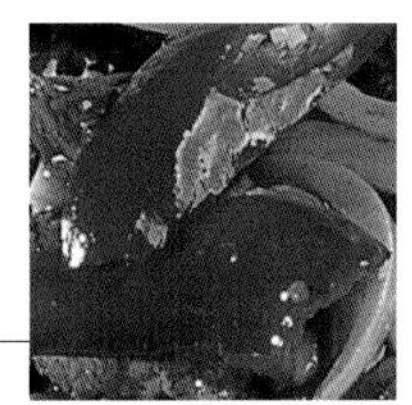

400g veal • a pinch of salt • black pepper • 100g onion • 1 clove garlic • 4 fresh red chillis • 175 ml vegetable stock • 2 tbsps light soya sauce • 2 tbsps oyster sauce • 2 tbsps rice wine

1 Cut the veal into thin bite-size strips. Season. Finely dice the onion, crush the garlic and shred the chillis. **2** Heat 2 tbsps of stock in a wok or heavy-based frying-pan until it begins to boil. Add the garlic and onion, and fry for 2-3 minutes or until dry. Add a little more stock and repeat. **3** Add the veal and chillis, and continue cooking, stirring continuously for another 2-3 minutes. Add a little more stock as necessary, repeating the process until the veal is cooked through. **4** Season with rice wine, soya sauce and oyster sauce. Bring to the boil and serve. **5** Garnish the dish with a little spring onion and Thai basil. Serve with steamed rice.

Medallions of Veal with Thyme

190 Calories • 4.4g Fat • Serves 4

400g veal loin, trimmed of all fat and sinew • black pepper • 80g carrots, cut into rounds • 80g turnips, cut into rounds • 1 tsp fresh thyme • 100g asparagus • 12 shallots, whole • 25g spring onions, chopped • 125ml meat glaze

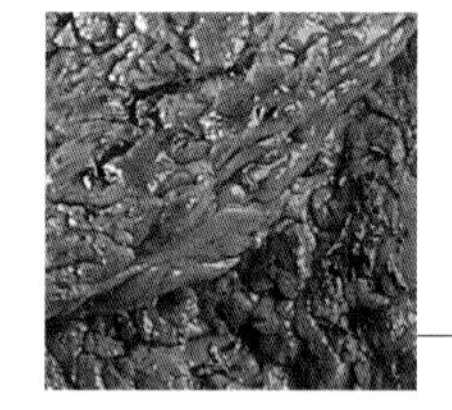

1 Season veal with pepper and half of the fresh thyme. **2** Blanch carrots, turnips, asparagus and shallots separately in boiling water. Refresh. **3** In a non-stick frying-pan, cook the meat (without using oil) with blanched shallots until done. Set aside to rest. **4** To make the sauce, simmer the spring onions and thyme in a little water until the onion is transparent. **5** Add the meat glaze and any juices from the cooked meat and bring to the boil. Adjust consistency if necessary. **6** To serve, spoon the sauce onto each plate and top this with the meat. Arrange the shallots and reheated vegetables around. Garnish with fresh thyme and serve.

Chicken Provençale

260 Calories • 4.4g Fat • Serves 4

400g chicken breasts • 2 onions • 200g stewed tomatoes, chopped • 3 cloves garlic, crushed • 125ml vegetable stock • 1 tsp salt substitute (see page 140) • ½ small carrot, finely diced • ½ stick celery, finely diced • 1 bay leaf

1 Peel and finely dice the onion. Place in a saucepan together with the crushed garlic and half of the vegetable stock and cook until soft. **2** Add the finely diced carrot and celery, and cook for 1-2 minutes without letting them turn in colour. **3** Add the chopped tomatoes. Cover and simmer for 5 minutes. **4** Add the chicken breasts, bay leaf, seasonings and remaining vegetable stock to the pan. Cover and simmer again until the chicken is tender. Serve with steamed vegetables or rice.

Thai-Style Green Chicken Curry

200 Calories • 4.8g Fat • Serves 4

400g chicken breasts • 125ml vegetable stock • 125ml low-fat milk • 3 tsps green curry paste (see page 141) • 5 green chillis • 40g pea aubergine • 80g white eggplant or aubergine • 15g Thai basil • 4 lime leaves • 1 tbsp nam pla (or light soya sauce)

1 Slice the chicken breasts. Shred the chillis and cut the white eggplant into quarters. **2** In a heavy-based pan, gently fry the curry paste with about 2 tablespoons of the vegetable stock, until the mixture becomes almost dry. **3** Add the chicken slices and coat thoroughly with the paste. Continue to cook adding the stock a little at a time, to prevent the meat from sticking. **4** Add the remaining stock, fresh chillis, pea aubergine, eggplant and nam pla. Simmer the curry for 3-5 minutes, or until the eggplants are cooked. **5** Finally add the basil and milk, heat and serve. Garnish with extra shredded chillis and basil.

Tip: Once the milk is added, simply heat the chicken curry through. Do not allow it to boil, or the milk will separate.

Tandoori-Style Chicken

280 Calories • 4.5g Fat • Serves 4

4 x 100g chicken breasts, skinless • 65ml low-fat yoghurt • 1 tbsp lime juice • 2 cloves garlic, crushed • 1 tbsp fresh ginger, grated • 1/2 tsp paprika • 1/2 tsp ground cumin seed • 1/2 tsp bird chilli, chopped • 200g mixed steamed rice (white, brown and wild grains)

1 In a blender, mix the yoghurt, lime juice, garlic, ginger, paprika, cumin and chilli to a paste. Spread this over the chicken breasts and leave to marinate for 1-2 hours or overnight, turning occasionally. **2** To cook, grill or bake the chicken breasts in the oven for 5-6 minutes at 180°C/350°F/Gas Mark 4, then turn, baste with the yoghurt mix and continue cooking for a further 5-6 minutes. **3** To serve, slice the chicken thickly and arrange slices on each plate. **4** Gently warm the remaining yoghurt and pour or brush over the chicken. Serve with steamed rice.

Lamb in Filo Pastry with Mustard Seed Sauce

340 Calories • 9.1g Fat • Serves 4

4 x 100g lamb loin fillets, trimmed • 4 sheets filo pastry • 1 tbsp low-fat yoghurt • 1 tsp green peppercorn mustard • 4 tbsps meat glaze (made by reducing fresh veal or chicken stock by ¾) • 4 medium potatoes • 100g spinach

1 Smear a little of the mustard onto the lamb. Wrap a sheet of the filo pastry around each piece of lamb. Seal the ends with a little yoghurt. Brush any remaining yoghurt over the top. Bake in a moderate oven, at 180°C/400°F/Gas Mark 4 for 12-15 minutes, or until the filo pastry has browned. Take care not to overcook the lamb parcels. **2** Meanwhile, cook the vegetables. Combine remaining mustard with the prepared meat glaze and heat through. **3** When the lamb is done, remove from the oven and set aside for 5 minutes in a warm place. **4** To serve, place a spoonful of the sauce at the front of the plate and then cut the lamb in half at an angle and place the slices over the sauce, cut side facing forward. Arrange the vegetables behind, and serve.

Pat King
Thai-Style Mushrooms with Ginger

70 Calories • 0.6g Fat • Serves 4

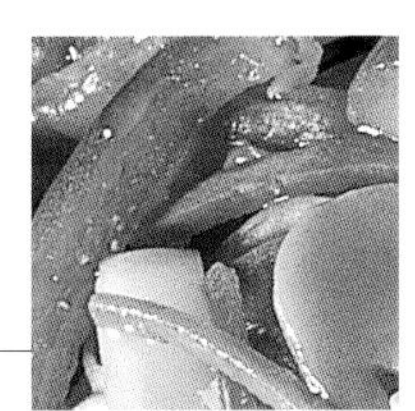

2 cloves garlic • 125g straw mushrooms • 180g oyster mushrooms • 10g wood ear • 2 onions • 2 carrots • 1 bell pepper • 5cm fresh ginger • 2 spring onions • 2 tsps soya sauce • 125ml vegetable stock • fresh coriander

1 Soak the wood ear in hot water for 10 minutes. Drain. **2** Crush the garlic. Shred the carrots, onions and bell pepper. Chop the spring onions and cut the ginger into fine matchsticks. **3** Heat a wok or heavy-based frying-pan until very hot. Add 2 tablespoons of the stock and the crushed garlic. Stir quickly to cook through. **4** Add shredded vegetables and ginger, and cook for one minute. Add the mushrooms (cut in half if too big) and cook for a further 30 seconds. **5** Add the remaining stock and soya sauce. Bring to the boil and serve immediately, garnished with fresh coriander.

Tip: Take care that the vegetables remain crunchy.

Thai-Style Sweet and Sour Vegetables

120 Calories • 0.9g Fat • Serves 4

125ml vegetable stock • 300g sweetcorn • 4 spring onions, chopped • 150g pineapple, diced • 1 cucumber, deseeded and diced • 2 bell peppers • 1 onion, diced • 3 tomatoes, deseeded • 2 small chillis • 2 tbsps soya sauce • seasoning • 1 tsp cornflour

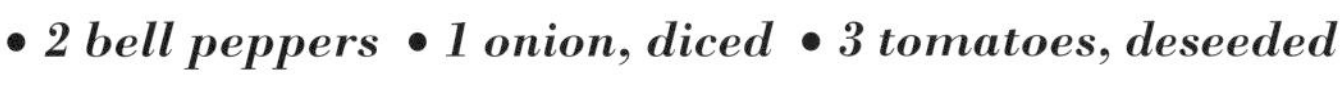

1 Place vegetable stock and diced onion, in a saucepan, and bring to the boil. Add the sweetcorn, cucumber, pineapple, bell pepper and tomatoes. Cover and simmer until soft, but not overcooked. **2** Add chopped spring onions, chillis, soya sauce and season to taste. **3** Add a little more vegetable stock if the combined ingredients are too dry. Simmer for a further 1-2 minutes. **4** Thicken with the cornflour, reboil and serve.

Tip: If the pineapple is ripe, no sweetener will be required. If it is not full flavoured, add up to one teaspoon of sugar, at 15 calories per tsp.

Chick Pea Curry with Vegetables

240 Calories • 2.4g Fat • Serves 4

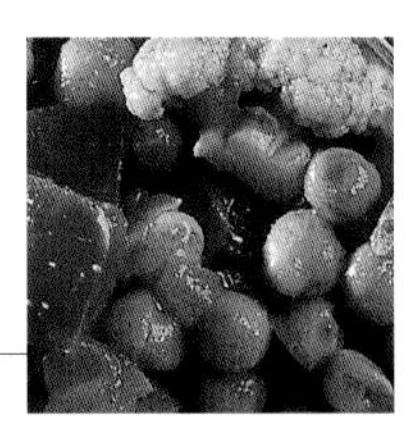

250ml vegetable stock • 100g onion, diced • 3 cloves garlic • $2^1/2$ tsp curry powder • 1 tsp cumin • a pinch of cayenne pepper • 150g cauliflower • 125ml water • 150g tomatoes, roughly chopped • 270g chick peas, cooked • 150g green peas • seasoning

1 In a saucepan, simmer 50ml vegetable stock, onion and garlic together, until the onion is cooked, and then increase the heat to evaporate the liquid. **2** Add the spices and dry-fry with the onion. Add a little more vegetable stock if the spices start to stick to the pan. **3** Add the remaining stock, cauliflower, tomatoes and water. Cover and simmer for 3-4 minutes. **4** Add the chick peas and green peas. Continue to cook until the curry is heated through, and peas are tender. Adjust seasoning.

Indian-Style Vegetable Samosas

260 Calories • 1.0g Fat • Serves 4

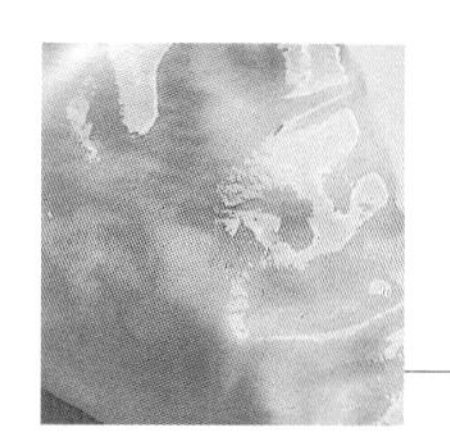

2 large potatoes • 2 onions • 1 tsp fresh ginger • 1/2 tsp fennel seeds • 1/2 tsp ground coriander • 1/4 tsp curry powder • 1/8 tsp cumin • 1/8 tsp turmeric • a pinch of cayenne pepper • 300g green peas • 4 sheets filo pastry • 1 tbsp low-fat yoghurt

1 Cut the potatoes into cubes, the same size as the peas and then blanch. Drain and put to one side. **2** Blanch the peas. **3** In a non-stick frying-pan, place 2 tsps water and all the spices. Fry until fragrant, adding a little more water if necessary. **4** Add the potatoes and peas, and mix well. **5** Take one sheet of filo pastry and cut in half lengthways. Fold in half again lengthways and place a spoonful of the vegetable mix on one end. Starting with the vegetables, fold up the filo pastry in a triangular fashion. **6** Brush the pastry ends and top with a little yoghurt. Place on a non-stick baking sheet. Repeat the samosas with the remaining pastry. **7** Air-dry for 20-30 minutes before baking at 180°C/350°F/Gas Mark 4 for 12-15 minutes or until golden brown. Serve warm.

Chilli Pumpkin

200 Calories • 1.6g Fat • Serves 4

2 cloves garlic, crushed • 2 shallots, shredded • 3-4 chillis (to taste) • 3 kaffir lime leaves • 8 cups pumpkin, peeled and cut into 1cm cubes • 3 tbsps soya sauce • 2 tbsps Chinese wine • 250ml vegetable stock • fresh Thai basil

1 In a wok or heavy-based frying-pan, heat a little stock and cook the garlic, shallots and chillis for a few moments. **2** Add the remaining ingredients, except the basil and stir-fry until done. Add a little extra stock if too dry and the pumpkin is not yet cooked. **3** Lastly, add the shredded basil.

Moroccan-Style Chick Pea Stew

285 Calories • 2.0g Fat • Serves 4

3 onions • 2 cloves garlic • 2 carrots • 1 green bell pepper • 1 tsp ground cumin • 1/2 tsp fresh ginger • 1/2 tsp cayenne pepper (to taste) • 1/4 tsp ground cinnamon • 80g eggplant, diced • 3 tomatoes • 200g chick peas • 200g couscous, cooked • 350ml vegetable stock (variable)

1 Soak the chick peas in water overnight to soften. **2** Prepare the vegetables. Cut them all into 1cm cubes. Into a saucepan, pour a quarter of the vegetable stock. Add the spices and garlic, and fry until dry. **3** Drain the chick peas and mix these with the spice paste. Cook for 1-2 minutes. Add a little more stock, and the onions and carrots. Cook for 2-3 minutes. **4** Add remaining vegetables and stock, and mix well. Cover and simmer until tender. Add a little more stock or water, if the mixture becomes too dry. **5** When cooked, check seasoning, and adjust the taste if necessary. Serve the stew piping hot with the cooked couscous.

Baked Potato Stuffed with Spinach

320 Calories • 2.1g Fat • Serves 4

4 baking potatoes • 800g cooked spinach • 50g lowfat ricotta cheese • 1 tbsp parsley, chopped • nutmeg • pepper • salt substitute (see page 140) • 50g wholewheat breadcrumbs

1 Wash potatoes and bake in a moderate oven, 180°C/350°F/Gas Mark 4 for 30-35 minutes or until soft. Remove and set aside to cool. **2** Meanwhile blanch the spinach. Squeeze out all excess moisture from the spinach. Mix with the ricotta and parsley. Season with pepper, nutmeg and salt substitute to taste. **3** Cut tops off potatoes, scoop out the flesh and mash. Mix this with the prepared spinach mix and refill back into the potato skins. **4** Sprinkle the stuffed potatoes with breadcrumbs and heat in the oven until the topping is golden.

Stir-Fried Glass Noodles

195 Calories • 5.5g Fat • Serves 4

250g dried glass noodles • 60g bean sprouts • 80g carrots • 5ml oil • 6 dried red chillis • 100g firm tofu • 1cm fresh ginger • 1 tsp sugar • 4 spring onions • 2 tbsps nam pla (or soya sauce) • 4 tbsps lime juice • 10g roasted almonds, chopped • fresh coriander • 4 cloves garlic

1 Soak the noodles in hot water for 5 minutes. Drain. Finely chop the garlic and ginger. In a wok, heat the oil and stir-fry the chillis, garlic and ginger. Shred the carrots and add to the wok. Toss and remove. **2** Cut the tofu into cubes, add to the wok and cook until they have coloured. Remove. **3** Add the carrot mixture back to the wok, finely chop the spring onions and add these together with the sugar, nam pla and lemon juice. Bring to the boil. **4** Add the noodles to the wok and heat through. Add the cubed tofu and fresh coriander. Toss together well and serve.

Fried Wild Rice

330 Calories • 1.1g Fat • Serves 4

600g wild rice • 2 sticks celery • 2 medium onions • 250ml vegetable stock • 2 green bell peppers • 2 cloves garlic, crushed • 1 carrot • 4 spring onions, chopped • 2 tbsps soya sauce • salt substitute (see page 140)

1 Finely dice the onion, carrot, celery and bell peppers. **2** In a wok or heavy-based frying-pan, add 2 tablespoons of the vegetable stock and heat through until the stock boils and starts to evaporate. Add the garlic and onion and a little more stock, then stir-fry. **3** Add the other vegetables progressively, adding stock as necessary. **4** Add the wild rice and mix well. Season to taste with soya sauce and salt substitute. **5** Fold the spring onions through the rice and serve.

Indonesian Noodles

265 Calories • 3.4g Fat • Serves 4

250g thin rice noodles • 1 onion, shredded • 3 cloves garlic • 60ml vegetable stock • 1 tsp fresh ginger • 60g bean sprouts • 150g snow peas • 2 tbsps soya sauce • 1 tsp chilli powder (to taste) • 1 tsp roasted almonds, chopped • red chilli

1 In a wok or heavy-based frying-pan, place the shredded onion and crushed garlic. Add half the vegetable stock and fry the onion until it has softened. **2** Add the ginger and noodles. Stirring quickly, fry until almost done. **3** Add the bean sprouts, remaining stock, peas, soya sauce and chilli powder. Mix together well and continue to cook for 1-2 minutes or until the peas are cooked but remain crunchy. **4** Serve sprinkled with the chopped nuts and finely shredded red chilli.

Tofu with Garlic and Pepper

165 Calories • 7.3g Fat • Serves 4

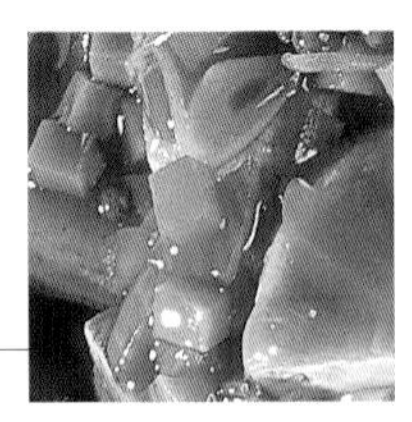

600g tofu • 250ml vegetable stock • 3 cloves garlic • 3 tbsps soya sauce • 2 carrots, finely diced • 2 onions, finely diced • ½ tsp black pepper • 2 tsps fresh green peppercorns • 1 tsp cornflour

1 Drain tofu well and pat dry. Cut into cubes. Heat a non-stick frying-pan, until very hot. Add the tofu and brown on one side. Turn the tofu over and brown the other side and repeat this process until all sides are done. **2** Add garlic, onions, carrots, soya sauce and a little of the vegetable stock. Cook for 2-3 minutes. **3** Add pepper (and green peppercorns, if using) and blend gently. **4** Mix the cornflour with a little water, and add to the pan to thicken the sauce.

Tip: If using tinned green peppercorns, wash them 3 times before using.

Thai-Style Potatoes with Ginger

280 Calories • 0.9g Fat • Serves 4

4 baking potatoes • 1 tsp cornflour • 250ml vegetable stock • 1 clove garlic • 160g mushrooms • 2 onions • 1 tbsp fresh ginger • 1 tsp soya sauce • 1 green bell pepper • 2 spring onions • 1/2 tsp apple juice concentrate • pepper

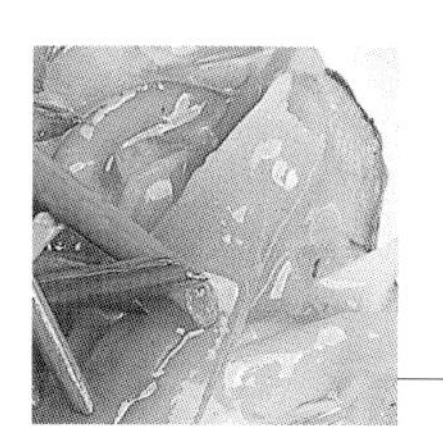

1 Bake potatoes in a moderate oven, 180°C/350°F/Gas Mark 4 until just cooked. Remove from the oven, cut into 1cm thick slices, lay on a non-stick baking sheet and continue to cook until they turn a golden colour. **2** Crush the garlic. In a saucepan, heat 2 tablespoons of the stock and fry the garlic. Shred the onions, mushrooms and green bell pepper and add them all to the stock with the ginger. Season with soya sauce, apple concentrate and pepper. **3** Mix the remaining vegetable stock with the cornflour and add to the pan. Bring to the boil. **4** To serve, place the crispy potato slices in a bowl and pour the sauce over. Garnish with chopped spring onions.

Thai-Style Spicy Long Beans

180 Calories • 1.0g Fat • Serves 4

600g green beans • 3 cloves garlic, crushed • 1 tsp red curry paste (see page 141) • 2 tbsps soya sauce • 125ml vegetable stock • 2 lime leaves, torn • 2 red chillis • 1 tsp Thai basil • 1 tsp cornflour • 200g steamed rice

1 Cut and trim beans to 3cm lengths. In a wok or heavy-based frying-pan, fry the crushed garlic with 3 tablespoons of vegetable stock. Add curry paste and beans and continue to cook. Add extra stock if required. **2** When beans are cooked add chillis, lime leaves, soya sauce and any remaining stock. Thicken slightly with the cornflour. **3** Add the basil, toss and serve with steamed rice.

Apple and Date Strudel

240 Calories • 1.1g Fat • Serves 6

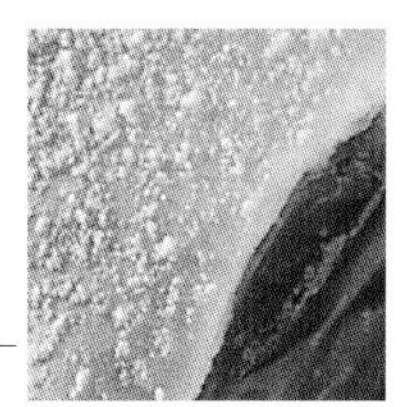

65ml apple concentrate • 1 tsp ground cinnamon • 1/4 tsp nutmeg • a pinch of ground cloves • 2 green cooking apples • 180g dates • 6 sheets filo pastry • 4 tbsps low-fat yoghurt • 3 tbsps wheatgerm

1 Warm the apple concentrate with the spices in a saucepan over a medium heat for 1-2 minutes. Leaving the skin on, slice the apples thinly and add to the liquid, together with the dates. Cook until soft, but not mushy. **2** Add 1 tablespoon of wheatgerm and set aside to cool. **3** Lay out the filo pastry and spread each sheet lightly with a little yoghurt. Sprinkle with 1/2 teaspoon of the wheatgerm, followed by another layer of pastry. Repeat the process until all the filo pastry is used. **4** Spread the cooled apple and date mix over the final layer of filo pastry. Roll up and place on a non-stick baking sheet, seam-side down. **5** Brush the strudel with any remaining yoghurt and bake in a moderate oven, 180°C/350°F/Gas Mark 4 for 12-15 minutes, or until lightly golden in colour.

Italian Ricotta Cheesecake

100 Calories • 5.0g Fat • Serves 18

3 tbsps toasted breadcrumbs • 2 eggs • 700g low-fat ricotta cheese • 2 tbsps lime juice • 2 tbsps orange juice • zest of 1 orange • zest of 1 lime • 350g yoghurt cheese (see page 140) • 50g sugar • 2 tbsps flour

BLUEBERRY COULIS: ***100g blueberries • 1 tsp apple concentrate***

1 Spread the breadcrumbs over the base of a round spring-bottom cake tin. **2** Blend all the remaining ingredients together. Pass through a sieve and pour into the prepared tin. **3** Cook in a bain-marie at 160°C/310°F/Gas Mark 3 for 40-45 minutes, or until the cheesecake is just firm in the centre. **4** After the cheesecake has cooled, gently run a warm knife around the edge and release the spring of the tin. Place on a plate, cut into slices and serve with blueberry coulis.

TO MAKE THE COULIS: Place the berries and apple concentrate in a saucepan. Slowly bring the fruit to the boil, purée and strain. Allow to cool before using.

Summer Pudding

160 Calories • 2.3g Fat • Serves 6

650g mixed berries (fresh or frozen)

• 2 tbsp apple concentrate (or honey)

• juice of 1 lime

• 8 slices of day-old bread • 50g ricotta cheese

1 Select half a cup of the best berries for use as a garnish and chill. Place the remaining berries in a saucepan with the lime juice and apple concentrate. Bring to the boil. **2** Meanwhile, remove the crusts from the bread and line a terrine or bread tin with 6 slices, ensuring they overlap. **3** Take half a cup of the cooked berries and purée these to make the sauce, then set aside. **4** Spoon the cooked berries into the lined terrine, pressing down as you go. Top with the remaining bread slices, and fold over the edges. **5** Weight down and refrigerate overnight. **6** To serve, whip the ricotta cheese until light and creamy. Slice the terrine and place a portion on each plate with some of the berry sauce spooned around. Garnish the slices with the chilled berries and a little of the whipped ricotta.

Apricot and Coconut Terrine

110 Calories • 3.4g Fat • Serves 4

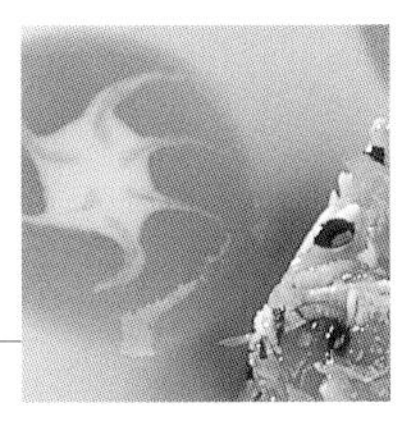

100g dried apricots • 25g carob chocolat
• 30ml honey • 15ml passion fruit (or orange) juice
• 25g shredded coconut, toasted
SAUCE: ***40g dried apricots • water***

1 Chop apricots and carob into small pieces. Mix with the honey, passion fruit and coconut. Line a terrine or mould with clingfilm and press the mixture into it firmly. Cover and chill for 2 to 3 hours. **2** To make the sauce, cover the apricots with water and slowly bring to the boil. Purée and strain. Cool. Serve a slice of the terrine on a plate with the apricot sauce poured around.

Cranberry Pudding

130 Calories • 0.3g Fat • Serves 6

300g cranberries (reserve a few for the garnish)
• 175g sugar • 2 tbsps cornflour
• 2 tbsps orange juice • 100g raspberries
• 1 tbsp low-fat yoghurt • fresh mint

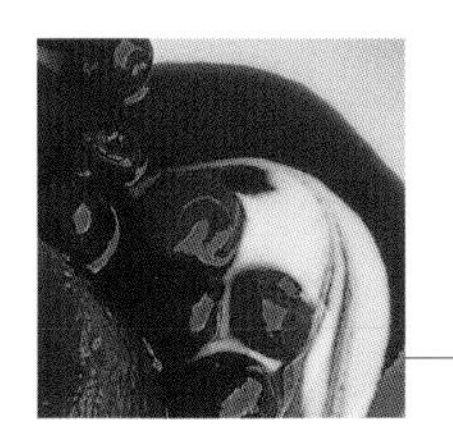

1 Place the cranberries and water in a saucepan. Bring to the boil and simmer for 15 minutes. Press through a sieve and discard the seeds and skins. Return the juice to the pan with the sugar. **2** Mix the cornflour with orange juice and add to the cranberry juice. Bring the juice to the boil and simmer, stirring continuously for 2 minutes. **3** Pour into small dessert moulds and chill. **4** To make sauce, purée the raspberries then strain to remove the seeds. **5** To serve, invert the mould onto the centre of a cold plate, and pour the berry coulis around. Decorate the pudding with a little yoghurt, a small sprig of mint and a few of the reserved cranberries.

Carob Ice-cream

75 Calories • 0.8g Fat • Serves 12

50g sugar • 65g water • 1 tsp gelatine powder • 650ml skimmed milk • 150ml non-fat milk powder • 3 tbsps carob powder • 1 tbsp vinegar

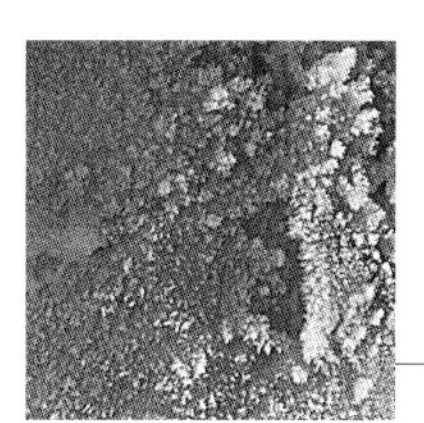

1 In a small saucepan, combine the carob powder with the sugar, water and gelatine and heat gently. Do not boil. Add the milk powder and pour into a large bowl. Add the skimmed milk, and chill. **2** When completely cold, pour the liquid into ice-cream trays and freeze. **3** When it has almost set, remove the ice-cream from the freezer and place in a food processor with the vinegar and process quickly until creamy. Return the mixture to the freezer trays and freeze until firm. Serve a few scoops in individual tuille baskets (see page 127).

Vanilla Ice-cream

65 Calories • 0.8g Fat • Serves 12

50g sugar • 65ml water • 1 tsp gelatine powder • 650ml skimmed milk • 150ml non-fat milk powder • 1 tbsp vinegar

1 In a small saucepan, combine the sugar, water and gelatine and heat gently. Do not boil. Add the milk powder and pour into a large bowl. Add the skimmed milk, and chill the liquid. **2** When completely cold, pour the liquid into ice-cream trays to freeze. **3** When almost set, remove from the freezer and place in a food processor with the vinegar and process quickly until creamy. Return to the freezer trays and freeze until firm. Serve in individual tuille baskets (see page 127).

Fresh Fruit Plate

135 Calories • 1.0g Fat • Serves 4

1 wedge cantaloupe melon • 1 small bunch grapes • ½ small papaya • 2 thick slices pineapple • 1 wedge of watermelon • 2 kiwi fruits • 2 limes • 4 sprigs of mint

1 Cut, peel and slice or carve the fruits as appropriate. Each fruit should be approximately the size of half a kiwi fruit. Each portion should be equivalent to 8 pieces of fruit. **2** Arrange decoratively on a plate, cover and chill well. **3** Garnish with half a lime and a sprig of mint.

Chequerboard Ice-cream

70 Calories • 0.8g Fat • Serves 12

1/2 recipe vanilla ice-cream (see page 123)
• 1/2 recipe carob ice-cream (see page 123)

1 Make both ice-creams according to the recipes on page 121 and freeze in trays 2cm deep. **2** When both ice-creams are frozen solid, remove them from the freezer and cut each flavour into 2cm-wide logs. You will need 5 vanilla and 4 carob logs. **3** Working quickly, arrange logs in alternating colours to produce a chequerboard block. **4** Wrap in clingfilm and return to the freezer. To serve, slice the log and place in centre of a cold plate with a little carob sauce poured around (see page 126).

Ice-cream Bombe

110 Calories • 2.0g Fat • Serves 6

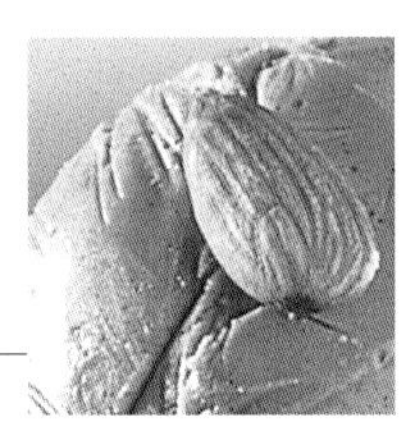

80g raisins • 2 tbsps sherry • 125ml skimmed milk • 1 tsp gelatine • 1 tsp instant coffee • 1 tsp cocoa • 1 tbsp roasted almonds, chopped • 1 tbsp sugar • 250ml low-fat yoghurt

CAROB SAUCE: ***180ml skimmed milk • 45g cottage cheese • 1 egg white • 2pkd equal • 1 tsp cornflour • 1 tsp carob powder***

1 Soak the raisins in sherry for 30 minutes. **2** Dissolve gelatine in a little warm water with the sugar. Combine milk, coffee, cocoa and yoghurt. Pour into an ice-cream machine, and churn until almost frozen. **3** Add the gelatine, almonds and soaked raisins. Continue to churn, until all ingredients are sufficiently blended, but no more. Spoon into containers and freeze. **4** Remove the ice-cream bombe from the freezer 5 minutes before serving. Serve with carob sauce and fresh mint leaves.

FOR THE CAROB SAUCE: Blend all ingredients together in a food processor until smooth. Pour the mixture into a saucepan and cook over a gentle heat until it thickens. Strain and chill.

Assorted Home-made Sorbets

80 Calories • 0.3g Fat • Serves 12

600ml fresh fruit purée (pineapple, peach, mango, strawberry, watermelon or any combination of your favourite fruit) • 100g sugar • 250ml water • 1 tbsp lime juice (optional)

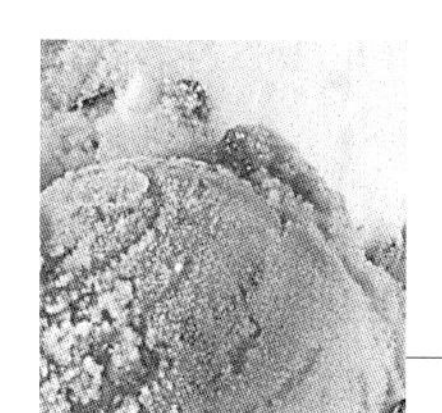

1 Bring water and sugar to the boil, and simmer until dissolved into a syrup. Cool. Add the fruit purée (and lime juice if a little sweet). **2** Pour into an ice-cream machine and churn until frozen. Store in the freezer until required. **3** To serve, arrange a scoop of three or more varieties in a tuille basket (see recipe below).

Tip: Depending on the fruit used, it may be necessary to cook the fruit pulp, to prevent discolouration. The easiest way is to add it to the sugar syrup and boil all the ingredients together for 1-2 minutes.

Tuille Baskets

50 Calories per basket • 1.8g Fat • Makes 12 baskets

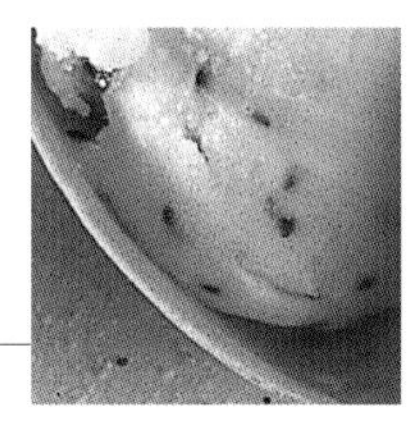

1 tsp honey • 40g brown sugar • 30g margarine • 60g flour • 1 egg white • zest of 1/2 an orange

1 Melt the margarine, and set aside. Add the honey and orange zest. **2** Beat the egg whites with 2 tablespoons of the sugar until the mixture doubles in volume. **3** Gradually beat in the remaining sugar, and carefully fold in the flour, cooled margarine and honey mix. Do not over mix. Set aside for 5 minutes before proceeding. **4** Make a template from thick plastic, cut to any desired shape. **5** Place the prepared template onto a non-stick baking tray, place a spoonful of the mixture in the centre, and with a spatula, spread out until approximately 3mm thick. Remove the template and repeat the process. **6** Bake the biscuit rounds at 200°C/400°F/Gas Mark 6 for 8-10 minutes, or until the baskets start turning golden around the edges. Remove from the oven, and with a spatula, quickly remove them from the tray before they harden. If you require them shaped, you should do this immediately. If they harden too quickly, you can return them to the oven to re-soften slightly.

Carrot and Honey Bread

70 Calories per roll • 0.6g Fat • Makes 28 rolls

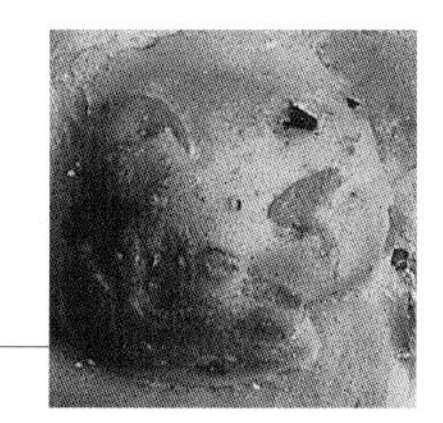

250ml low-fat milk • 270g flour • 270g wholemeal flour
• 1 tsp salt • 1 tsp brown sugar • 3 tsps dry yeast
• 1 egg • 3 tsps honey • 80g carrots, grated
• 1 tsp fresh ginger

1 Warm the milk in a saucepan and remove from the heat. Dissolve the yeast in the milk with the sugar and honey. Leave in a warm place to double in size. **2** Combine flours with salt, carrots and ginger. Make a well in the centre of the flour. **3** Beat the egg and pour into the yeast mixture. Pour the liquid into the flour well and mix to form a dough. Knead the dough until smooth and elastic. Cover with a cloth and place somewhere warm for 30 minutes to one hour to prove. **4** Knock back, divide into rolls, and shape into rolls. Leave to prove once again, then bake at 200°C/400°F/Gas Mark 6 for 10-12 minutes, or until the rolls turn a golden colour.

Bread Sticks

65 Calories per bread stick • 0.4g Fat • Makes approx 40 bread sticks

• 800g wholewheat flour
• 400ml water • 1 tsp salt
• 3 tsps yeast
• 1 tbsp pesto or 2 tbsps chopped fresh herbs

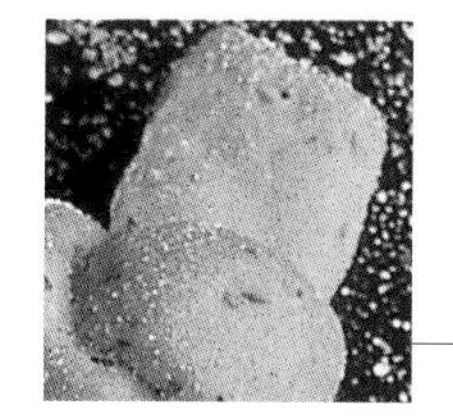

1 Warm the water to blood temperature. Dissolve yeast in a little of the water and leave to ferment. **2** Add salt to the flour and mix well. **3** Add the pesto to the yeast, then mix into the flour. Combine and knead into a smooth dough. Cover and leave aside in a warm place to rise for 30-45 minutes or until the dough doubles in volume. **4** Knock back and divide into portions. Shape and place on a floured baking tray. Leave to prove for 5 minutes in a warm place, then bake in a moderate oven at 180°C/350°F/Gas Mark 4 for 15 minutes until crispy and golden.

Sweetcorn and Chilli Bread

70 Calories per roll • 0.2g Fat • Makes 28 rolls

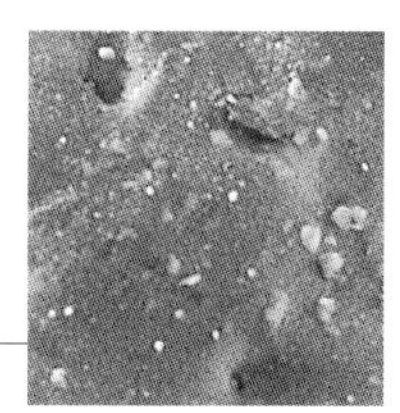

600ml water • 400g plain bread flour
• 135g wholewheat flour • 2 tsps dry yeast
• 1 tsp salt • 300g sweetcorn, fresh or frozen
• 150g jalapeno peppers, chopped • 2/3 tbsp cornflour

1 Dissolve yeast in warm water. Leave in a warm place to ferment. **2** Combine flours with the sweetcorn, peppers and cornflour. Add to the fermented yeast. **3** Combine ingredients well to form a dough. Knead until smooth and elastic. Cover dough with a damp cloth and leave to double in volume. Knock back, divide into rolls and place on a floured baking tray. **4** Prove until the rolls double in size, then bake at 200°C/400°F/Gas Mark 6 for 10-12 minutes or until golden in colour.

Mango Date Cake

Calories 100 • 0.3g Fat • Serves 12

120g flour • 130 wholewheat flour
• 1$^1/_2$ tsps baking powder
• $^1/_2$ tsp baking soda • 1$^1/_2$ mangoes • 1 banana
• 6 dates • 125ml apple concentrate

1 Purée the mangoes and banana together, chop the dates and combine with the remaining ingredients. **2** Pour into a 10in cake ring and bake at 150°C/300°F/Gas Mark 2 for 25-30 minutes.

Apricot Fudge

85 Calories • 0.7g Fat • Serves 16

50g flour • 50g oat bran • 50g cocoa
• 200g sugar • 100g pumpkin, cooked • 3 egg whites
• seeds of $^1/_2$ vanilla pod
• 180g dried apricots

1 Place apricots in a saucepan and just cover with water. Cover with a lid, bring to the boil then .remove from the heat and set aside for 5 minutes. Purée. **2** Meanwhile, combine flour, oat bran, cocoa, sugar, pumpkin, egg whites and vanilla seeds. Spread half of the mixture over the base of a 9in non-stick cake tin. Carefully spread the apricot purée on top, then finish with the remaining fudge mix. **3** Bake in the oven at 165°C/320°F/Gas Mark 3 for 15-20 minutes.

Moist Pineapple Cake

140 Calories • 0.2g Fat • Serves 16

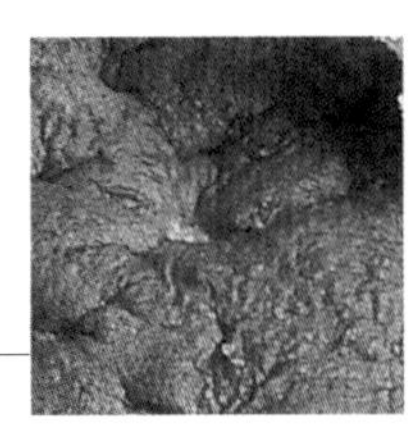

270g flour • 300g sugar • 1$^1/_2$ tsps baking soda
• 100g cooked pumpkin, mashed
• 250ml pineapple juice
• 125ml orange juice • 1 tsp vanilla essence

1 Mix the flour, sugar and baking soda together in a bowl. **2** Stir in the mashed pumpkin, pineapple juice, orange juice and vanilla essence. **3** Pour the prepared mixture into a 10in cake ring and bake at 160°C/310°F/Gas Mark 2 for 30-35 minutes.

Tip: As with all low-fat bakery items, care must be taken *not* to overcook the cake.

Orange and Pumpkin Crumb Cake

100 Calories • 0.5g Fat • Serves 12

120g flour • 70g wholewheat flour • 100g sugar • 1/4 tsp baking soda • 50ml orange juice • zest of 1 orange • 50g pumpkin, puréed (tinned) • 3 egg whites

TOPPING: ***50g oatmeal • 2 tbsps wheatgerm • 2 tsps brown sugar • 3 tsps orange juice***

1 Blend the two flours with the sugar, baking soda, orange juice, orange zest, pumpkin purée and egg whites. Pour the mixture into a non-stick baking tin. **2** Mix the oatmeal with the wheatgerm, brown sugar and orange juice to form a crumb topping. Spread this over the cake batter. **3** Bake at 150°C/300°F/Gas Mark 2 for 25-30 minutes. Cut into slices while still warm.

Chocolate Cake

100 Calories • 2.5g Fat • Serves 16

175g cocoa powder • 250ml choice of beverage • 4 egg yolks • 200g sugar • 6 egg whites • 120g flour • 150ml hot water

1 Dissolve the cocoa powder in the hot water then set aside to cool. **2** Place half the sugar in a bowl with the egg yolks. Beat together in the bowl over a boiling saucepan of water until thick and frothy. Remove from the heat and continue to beat until the mixture has cooled. **3** Add the cocoa solution. **4** Place the remaining 100g of sugar in a separate bowl with the egg whites and beat to the consistency of meringues. Then, alternating with the flour, fold the egg yolk mixture into the egg whites. **5** Pour the prepared mixture into a non-stick cake tin and bake at 180°C/350°F/Gas Mark 4 for 20-25 minutes or until the top of the cake feels firm yet spongy.

Carrot Cinnamon Cake

160 Calories • 0.3g Fat • Serves 16

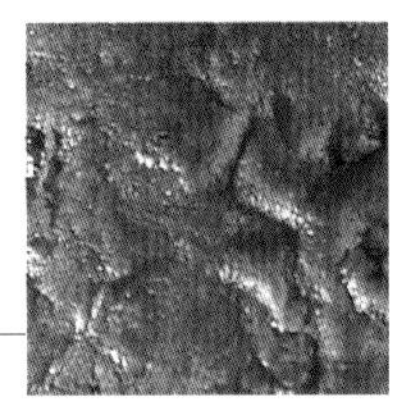

340g flour • 250g brown sugar

• 2 tsps baking powder

• 2 tsps cinnamon • 150ml apple juice

• 4 egg whites • 240g carrots, grated • 50g raisins

1 Mix all the dry ingredients together. Stir in the apple juice, egg whites, carrots and raisins.

2 Pour into a 10in cake ring and bake at 160°C/310°F/Gas Mark 2 for 30-35 minutes.

Honey Oat Bars

55 Calories • 0.5g Fat • Serves 12

210g instant rolled oats • 35g wholewheat flour • 35g wheatgerm • 1/4 tsp ground cinnamon • 75ml apple concentrate • 90g dried apricots

1 Chop the apricots and mix with the flours, rolled oats, apple concentrate and ground cinnamon. **2** Pack the mixture into an 8in square tin and bake in a moderate oven, at 150°C/300°F/Gas Mark 2 for 18-20 minutes. Cool and cut into bars to serve.

Chocolate and Orange Biscotti

40 Calories per slice • 1g Fat • Makes 48 slices

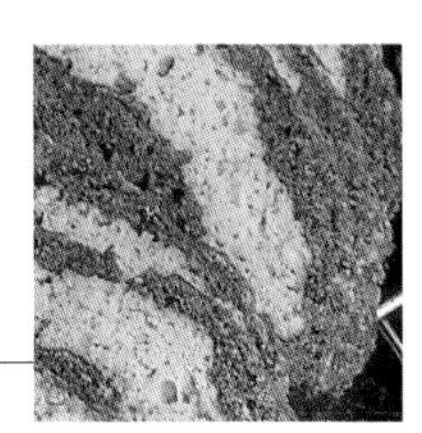

1 orange, zest and juice • 2 eggs • 2 tbsps oil • 1 tsp vanilla • 150g sugar • 200g flour • 50g cocoa powder • 1 tsp baking powder • a pinch of salt

1 Lightly beat the eggs in a bowl. Add the orange zest, orange juice, oil, vanilla, sugar, flour, baking powder and salt and work together to form a dough. **2** Divide into half, and to one half, add the cocoa powder as you knead the dough. Knead the other half. Shape the two pieces into logs, each approximately 4cm in diameter. Chill for at least 2 hours. **3** Place the cocoa-flavoured log onto the work surface, and gently flatten. Place the orange log on top, and carefully wrap the flattened cocoa log around it. **4** Place on a baking tray and bake at 180°C/350°F/Gas Mark 4 for 30-35 minutes, or until firm. Cool on a wire rack. **5** Cut into thin slices and bake again in a cool oven until dry and crisp. Store in an airtight container.

Thai Salad Dressing

15 Calories • 0.1g Fat • Serves 25

100g garlic • 50g fresh red chillis • 100g red bell peppers • 20g fresh coriander roots • 1 tbsp rice vinegar • 3 tbsps apple juice concentrate • seasoning to taste

1 Wash and clean the coriander roots. Carefully remove all the seeds from the chillis and the red bell peppers. **2** Place them all in a blender with the garlic and pulse blend. **3** Add the rice vinegar, apple juice concentrate and seasoning to taste.

Herb Salad Dressing

30 Calories • 0.2g Fat • Serves 15

125ml apple juice concentrate • 125ml cider vinegar • 2 tsps mustard powder • 1 clove garlic, crushed • 15g mixed fresh herbs, chopped

Combine all the ingredients together well. Store the dressing in the refrigerator.

Tip: This herb salad dressing will keep up to one month if always kept in the refrigerator.

Vegetable Stock

25 Calories per cup • 0.2g Fat per cup • Makes 1 litre

4 tomatoes • 1/4 small cabbage • 2 sticks of celery • 2 onions • 2 carrots • 1 litre water

Combine all the ingredients together and simmer for one hour. Strain, discarding the vegetables.

Roasted Garlic

40 Calories • 0g Fat • Serves 1

1 head of garlic

1 Take a whole head of garlic, and without peeling it wrap the head in clingfilm and steam for 30 minutes. **2** Remove from the heat and place the whole garlic in a moderate oven, 180°C/350°F/Gas Mark 4 and bake for 10-15 minutes. The actual cooking time depends on the accuracy of the oven temperature. Care should be taken to avoid burning the garlic skin. **3** Cut the head of the garlic globe off and serve warm as a side dish. Alternatively, remove the soft flesh from its skin and place in a glass jar. Stored correctly, it will keep for more than 2 weeks in the refrigerator.

Tip: Use as a replacement for butter.

Mayonnaise

15 Calories per tablespoon • 0.5g Fat • Makes approx. 250ml

125ml low-fat yoghurt • 1/2 tsp mustard powder • 2 tsps vinegar • 2 tbsps apple concentrate • 50g low-fat ricotta cheese

Place all the ingredients in a blender and blend together until smooth. Final results will depend on consistency of the yoghurt being used – a little extra ricotta may be required if the yoghurt is thin. Store in the refrigerator. The mayonnaise is best used within 2-3 days.

Environ Dressing

25 Calories per tablespoon • 0.6g Fat • Makes 250ml

125ml low-fat yoghurt • 1/2 tsp mustard powder • 2 tsps vinegar • 2 tbsps apple concentrate • 50g low-fat ricotta cheese • 1 tomato • 1 dill pickle • 1 small onion • 1/2 red bell pepper • 3 cloves garlic • 5 ml lime juice • a pinch of chilli powder

1 Combine the yoghurt, mustard, vinegar, apple concentrate and ricotta cheese in a food processor. Blend until it forms a smooth mayonnaise. **2** Peel and deseed the tomato. Dice the flesh. Dice the pickle, onion and bell pepper. Crush the garlic. **3** Add all ingredients to the mayonnaise, together with the lime juice and chilli powder. Mix well, and serve the mayonnaise with your favourite salad items.

Tip: If you are feeling a little lazy, the first five ingredients can be substituted with 125ml of low-fat commercial mayonnaise.

Yoghurt Cheese

65 Calories • 1.6g Fat • Serves 4

800ml low-fat yoghurt

1 Line a bowl with muslin cloth. Fill the cloth with yoghurt, and tie the cloth in a bundle. **2** Suspend the bundle over a sink (or bowl) for 5-6 hours, or until the whey has drained completely. Cool and store.

Tip: Fresh cheese should be used within two days.

Salt Substitute

5 Calories • 0.1g Fat • Serves 20

• 1 tsp cayenne pepper • 1 tsp garlic powder • 1 tsp dried basil • 1 tsp dried thyme • 1 tsp dried parsley flakes • 1 tsp ground mace • 1 tsp onion powder • 1 tsp ground black pepper • 1 tsp dried sage • 1 tsp dried marjoram

Mix all the ingredients together. Sprinkle the aromatic herbs into ingredients wherever the recipe indicates the use of salt substitute, and as a general seasoning for sauces and dressings.

Tip: This ingredient is also good for marinating fish and meat.

Red Curry Paste

• 20 Calories • 0.2g Fat • Serves 10

• 12 dried red chillis • 1 tbsp fresh lemon grass • 1 tbsp fresh galangal or ginger • 2 tsps coriander seeds • 1 tsp caraway seeds • 6 cloves garlic • 1 tsp shrimp paste • 4 kaffir lime leaves • 6 spring onions

1 Soak the coriander and cumin seeds in a little boiling water. Allow to soak until they soften a little. **2** Add the seeds to the remaining ingredients and place in a food processor, or pound in a mortar. If too dry, add a little of the soaked water. **3** Store in an airtight container.

Green Curry Paste

10 Calories • Fat 0.2g • Serves 10

• 3 lime leaves • 3 tsps pepper • 1 tsp coriander seeds • 70g green chilli • 6 cloves garlic • 1 tbsp fresh galangal or ginger • 2 spring onions • 1/4 lime • 1/2 tsp sugar

1 Soak the coriander seeds in a little boiling water, until they soften a little. **2** Drain, retaining the water on one side, and place the seeds with the remaining ingredients in a food processor, or pound in a mortar. If too dry, add a little of the soaked water. **3** Store in an airtight container.

List of Recipes

FLY SMOOTH AS SILK TO EXOTIC THAILAND
ON A ROYAL ORCHID HOLIDAY.

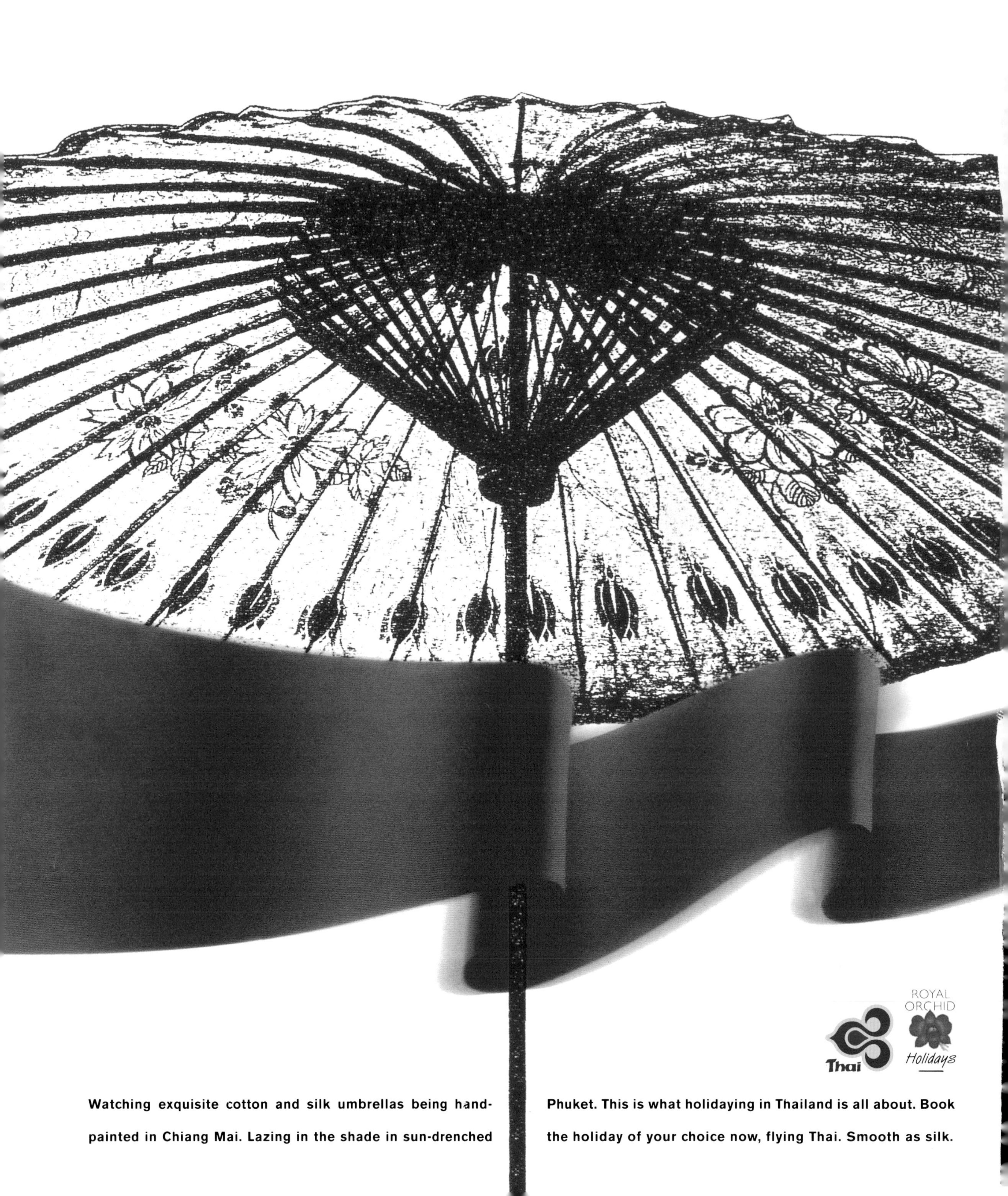